SKILLS FOR EVERYDAY LIFE

Terry Overton

WALCH PUBLISHING

2   3   4   5   6   7   8   9   10

ISBN 0-8251-1674-0

Contents

(continued)

Unit III—Measuring *(continued)*

Unit IV—Resources **77**

Unit V—Map Reading **89**

Unit VI—Problem-Solving 119

Unit I—Time

Time Frames

> **Introduction:** Each day you do many things. You go to school and other places. You have a time to do each thing. The story below is about Jason's day. Read the story. Then answer the questions about time.

Jason got ready for bed. He set his clock for 7:00 A.M. He wanted to be ready for school early. He would be going on a trip with his class. His class was going to the TV station.

Jason turned off the light. He went to sleep before 10:00 P.M.

In the morning the clock rang. Jason turned off the clock. He got up fast. He dressed and ate breakfast.

Jason left his house. He walked to the corner and waited for the bus. The bus came by at 8:00 A.M. Jason rode the bus to school.

When Jason got to school he saw John. Jason and John walked to their class. At 8:30 A.M. Jason's class left the school. The class rode the bus to the TV station.

Inside the TV station were many things. Jason saw cameras and clocks. He saw ladders and lights. He met many people.

Jason's class left the TV station at noon. The class went to the park. Jason's class ate lunch in the park.

(continued)

Time Frames (continued)

After lunch, Jason's class went back to school. Jason's next class was math at 1:30 P.M.

In math class Jason added numbers. After math Jason went outside. He played football with John.

The bell rang at 2:00 P.M. Jason and John went to class. Jason's class was reading. Jason read his story.

Jason's teacher said it was time to go home. It was 3:00 P.M. Jason put his books away. The bell rang. Jason went to his bus. Jason rode the bus home.

Jason got home at 4:00 P.M. He did his homework. Jason was hungry. He ate dinner at 5:30 P.M.

At 6:30 P.M. Jason looked outside. It was dark. Jason stayed in his house. He read a book until 8:00 P.M.

* *

Time Frames Activity

Answer the questions below.

1. What was the first thing Jason did in this story?

   _____

   _____

2. For what time did Jason set his clock?

   _____

   _____

3. Jason went to sleep before what time?

   _____

   _____

Time Frames Activity (continued)

4. List the things that Jason did in the morning before he got to school.

a. _____

b. _____

c. _____

d. _____

e. _____

f. _____

g. _____

5. Complete the chart below. Tell about the things that Jason did in the story.

Time		What did Jason do?
morning	7:00 A.M.	_____
	8:00 A.M.	_____
	8:30 A.M.	_____
noon	12:00 noon	_____
	1:30 P.M.	_____
	2:00 P.M.	_____
afternoon	3:00 P.M.	_____
	4:00 P.M.	_____
	5:30 P.M.	_____
evening	6:30 P.M.	_____
night	8:00 P.M.	_____

(continued)

Time Frames Activity (continued)

6. What time of day do you do things? Fill in the chart below.
   Tell what you do for the times below.

Time		What do I do?
morning	7:00 A.M.	_____
	8:00 A.M.	_____
	8:30 A.M.	_____
noon	12:00 noon	_____
	1:30 P.M.	_____
	2:00 P.M.	_____
afternoon	3:00 P.M.	_____
	4:30 P.M.	_____
	5:30 P.M.	_____
evening	6:30 P.M.	_____
night	8:00 P.M.	_____

Using Time Frames

Introduction: Each day you have things to do. You go to school on weekdays. You have things to do at home. You may work. You will have more to do as you grow older. You want to go to school and work on time. You do not want to be late. You do not want to miss going to do things. You need to know more about time. Read the story below.

Linda has many things to do each day, Monday through Friday. She wakes up at 7:30 A.M. She dresses and then eats breakfast. She walks to school at 8:30 A.M. She is in class all morning. She eats lunch at 12:30 P.M. She has class from 1:30 to 3:30 P.M. Linda goes to work at 4:00 P.M. She works each day from 4:00 until 6:00 P.M. She eats dinner at 6:30 P.M. Linda works on homework from 7:30 until 9:30 P.M. She goes to sleep by 10:30 P.M.

On Saturday Linda wakes up at 8:00 A.M. She goes to work at 9:00 P.M. She has a lunch break at 12:00 noon. She goes back to work at 1:00 P.M. She goes home at 4:00 P.M. This Saturday she is going to eat dinner with Pam at 6:00 P.M. Linda and Pam will go to the movies at 7:30. Linda will go home at 9:30.

This Sunday morning Linda wakes up at 8:00 A.M. She dresses for church and eats breakfast. She goes to church at 10:00 A.M. After church, about 11:30, she will go with her parents on a trip. Linda will go with her parents to visit her grandmother. Linda will be at her grandmother's house at 1:00 P.M. She and her parents will stay at her grandmother's house until 5:00 P.M. Linda will be back at home by 6:30 P.M. She will eat dinner. At 7:30 P.M. Linda will work on housework until 9:30 P.M.

(continued)

Using Time Frames (continued)

Read each sentence below. For the blank in each sentence, write a *B* for Before or an *A* for After. Use the story to help you with the answers.

Like this: Linda walked to school ___A___ she ate breakfast.

The story says that Linda walked to school *after* she ate breakfast.

1. Linda's morning classes are _____ she eats lunch.

2. Linda goes to work _____ her afternoon classes.

3. Linda eats dinner during the week _____ she works.

4. Linda works _____ she does her homework.

5. Linda goes to eat dinner _____ she goes to the movies on Saturday.

6. Linda goes to her grandmother's house _____ she goes to church.

7. Linda goes to her grandmother's house _____ she goes home.

8. During the week, Linda goes to bed _____ she does her homework.

9. Linda dresses _____ she eats breakfast.

10. On Saturday Linda works _____ she goes to eat dinner with Pam.

* *

Using Time Frames Activity

Linda wanted to plan her week. Use the story about Linda to write the answers. Write in the things Linda must do.

(continued)

Using Time Frames Activity (continued)

Plan for weekdays—Monday through Friday.

Time	*Things to do—Monday-Friday*
7:30 A.M.	_____
8:30 A.M.	_____
8:30 A.M. to 12:30 P.M.	_____
12:30 to 1:30 P.M.	_____
1:30 to 3:30 P.M.	_____
4:00 P.M.	_____
4:00 to 6:00 P.M.	_____
6:30 to 7:30 P.M.	_____
7:30 to 9:30 P.M.	_____
10:00 P.M.	_____

Plan for weekends—Saturday and Sunday.

Time	*Things to do—Saturday*
8:00 A.M.	_____
9:00 A.M.	_____
9:00 A.M. to 12:00 noon	_____
12:00 noon to 1:00 P.M.	_____
1:00 to 4:00 P.M.	_____
6:00 to 7:30 P.M.	_____
7:30 to 9:30 P.M.	_____

(continued)

Using Time Frames Activity (continued)

Plan for weekends—Saturday and Sunday.

Time	Things to do—Sunday
8:00 A.M.	_____
9:00 A.M.	_____
9:00 A.M.to 12:00 noon	_____
12:00 noon to 1:00 P.M.	_____
1:00 to 4:00 P.M.	_____
6:00 to 7:30 P.M.	_____
7:30 to 9:30 P.M.	_____

Time by the Hour

When you tell time, you must read the clock. To read a clock, you must look first for the small hand or arrow. The small hand will tell you the hour. When the long hand or arrow points to 12, it means the time is right (exactly) at the hour.

This clock shows 1:00.

This clock shows 2:00.

This clock shows 3:00.

This clock shows 4:00.

(continued)

Time by the Hour (continued)

What are the times for these clocks? Write the answers below each clock.

1.

_____

2.

_____

3.

_____

4.

_____

5.

_____

6.

_____

Time by the Hour Activity

Part A:

Write the times of each clock below.

1.

_____

2.

_____

3.

_____

4.

_____

5.

_____

6.

_____

Part B:

Draw the hands for each clock below.

1. 6:00
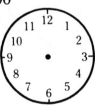
_____

2. 7:00

_____

3. 10:00
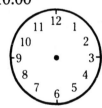
_____

4. 4:00
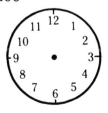
_____

5. 9:00
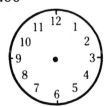
_____

6. 2:00
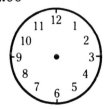
_____

Time by the Half-Hour

When you read a clock that has the hour time on it, the long hand is on the 12. When the long hand is halfway around the circle like this:

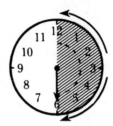

it is half past the hour.

This clock is half past 1:00, or 1:30.

This clock is half past 2:00, or 2:30.

This clock is half past 3:00, or 3:30.

(continued)

Time by the Half-Hour (continued)

When a clock is half past the hour, the little hand is halfway between 2 numbers.

Look at the clocks on the previous page. Where is the little hand when it is 1:30?

_____

Look at the next clock. Where is the little hand when it is 2:30?

_____

Look at the next clock. Where is the little hand when it is 3:30?

_____

There are 60 minutes in each hour. If the long hand is halfway around the clock, half of the 60 minutes have passed. A clock with the long hand halfway around, or half past an hour, has traveled (or gone by) 30 minutes. So 30 minutes is half of the hour. And 30 minutes is half of 60 minutes.

If the long hand is halfway around, 30 minutes have passed. This is also called 30 minutes past the hour.

A clock like this means 6:30, or half past 6 o'clock.

A clock like this means half past 7 o'clock, or 7:30.

(continued)

Time by the Half-Hour (continued)

What are the times of these clocks?

1.

Half past 9 means _____ : _____ .

2.

Half past _____ , or 10:30.

3.

Half past 11, or _____ : _____ .

Time by the Half-Hour Activity

Part A.

Write the times of each clock below.

1.

2.

3.

_____

4.

5.

6.

_____

Part B.

Draw the hands for each clock below.

1. 6:30

2. 8:30

3. 5:30

4. 10:30

5. 4:30

6. 11:30

Time by the Quarter-Hour

A clock that has the hour time on it has the long hand on the 12. When it is half past the hour, the long hand is on the 6, or halfway around the clock. The clock can be divided into halves for half past the hour like this:

This shows the 2 halves of the clock. Each half is 30 minutes long. The whole hour is 60 minutes long.

The clock can also be divided in quarters, like this:

Each quarter is 15 minutes long.

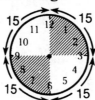

When the long hand points to the 3, it is 15 minutes past the hour.

This clock shows 1:15, or 15 minutes past the hour of 1:00.

(continued)

Time by the Quarter-Hour (continued)

This clock shows 2:15, or 15 minutes past the hour of 2:00.

This clock shows 5:15, or 15 minutes past the hour of 5:00.

When the long hand is on the 9, it shows 45 minutes past the hour, or 15 minutes before the next hour.
This clock shows 3:45, or 15 minutes before 4:00.

This clock shows 6:45, or 15 minutes before 7:00.

What time do these clocks show?

1.   2.   3.

_____   _____   _____

Time by the Quarter-Hour Activity

Part A.

These clocks show the time that passes for 2 hours. Write the times below the clocks.

1.

_____

2.

_____

3.

_____

4.

_____

5.

_____

6.

_____

7.

_____

8.

_____

9.

_____

(continued)

Time by the Quarter-Hour Activity (continued)

Part B.

Draw the hands to show the times below.

1.   10:15

———————————

2.   10:45

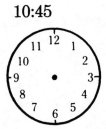

———————————

3.   6:15

———————————

4.   6:45

———————————

5.   9:15

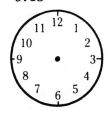

———————————

6.   9:45

———————————

Time by 5's

A clock that shows the hour time has the long hand on the 12.

This clock shows the hour of 3 o'clock.

A clock that shows half past the hour, or 30 minutes past, has the long hand on the 6.

This clock shows the time of 3:30.

A clock that shows 15 minutes after the hour, or a quarter past the hour, has the long hand on the 3.

This clock shows the time of 3:15.

A clock that shows 45 minutes after the hour has the long hand on the 9.

This clock shows the time of 3:45.

(continued)

Time by 5's (continued)

Between each set of numbers on the clock are 5 minutes. It takes 5 minutes for the long hand to travel from the 1 to the 2. It takes 5 minutes for the long hand to travel from the 2 to the 3.

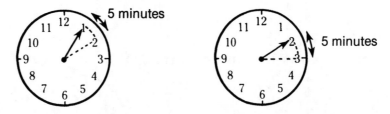

How many minutes will it take for the long hand to travel from the 3 to the 4?

1.

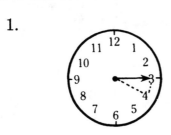

From the 4 to the 5?

2.

This clock shows 2:05, 5 minutes past 2:00.

(continued)

Time by 5's (continued)

This clock shows 4:05, 5 minutes past 4:00.

This clock shows 10 minutes after 8:00.

This clock shows 25 minutes after 10:00.

To tell time, count by 5's.
This clock shows how to count by 5's.

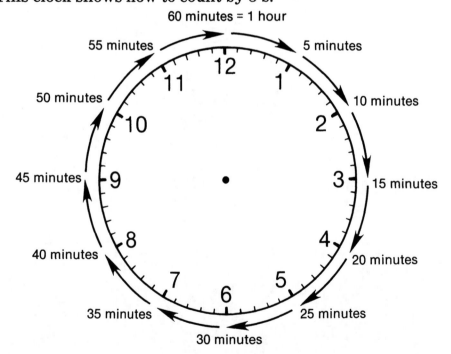

Time by 5's Activity

Part A.

Count by 5's. On each blank line, write the number of minutes that have passed when the long hand travels from the 12.

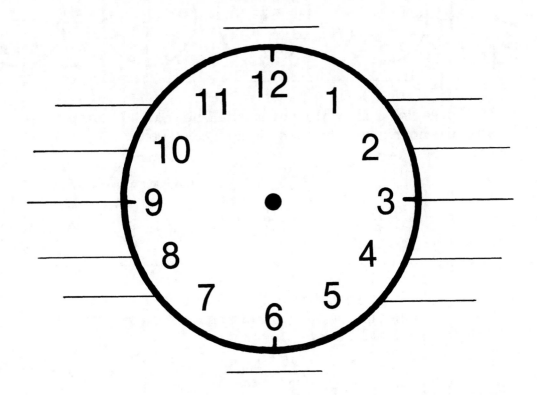

Part B.

Write the times for the clocks below.

1.   2.   3.   4.

Time by the Minute

I. These clocks show the long hand on the 12. These clocks show time by the hour. Write the time for each clock below.

_____ _____ _____ _____ _____

II. These clocks show time by the half-hour, or 30 minutes after the hour. Write the time for each clock below.

_____ _____ _____ _____ _____

III. These clocks show times that are one quarter-hour before the hour, or one quarter-hour past the hour. Write the time for each clock below.

_____ _____ _____ _____ _____

IV. These clocks show time as it passes every 5 minutes. Write the time for each clock below.

_____ _____ _____ _____ _____

(continued)

Time by the Minute (continued)

V. There are 60 minutes in a whole hour. These clocks show time by the minute. Write the time for each clock below.

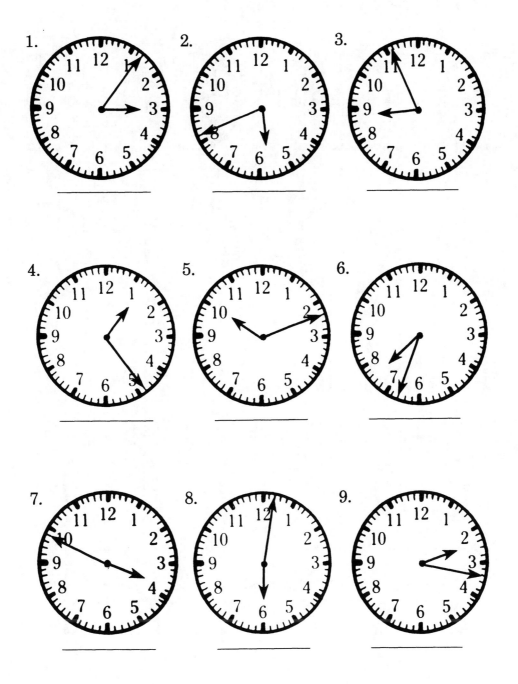

Time by the Minute Activity

Part A.

Write the time of each clock below.

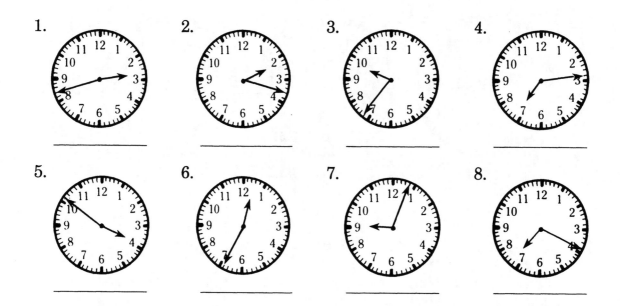

1. _____

2. _____

3. _____

4. _____

5. _____

6. _____

7. _____

8. _____

Part B.

Draw the hands on each clock below.

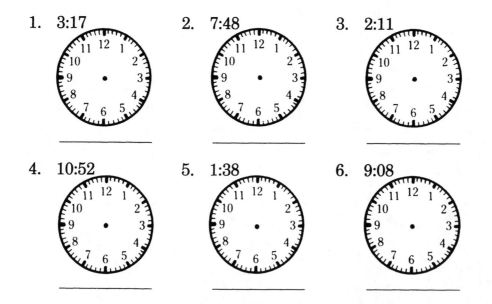

1. 3:17

2. 7:48

3. 2:11

4. 10:52

5. 1:38

6. 9:08

Unit II—Schedules

Review of Time Concepts

Each day you have things you do. Some days you go to school. You may work on other days. You may play sports on some days. You need to be on time each day.

Each day has parts. The sun rises at dawn. You awake and get ready for the day. You go to school in the morning. You eat lunch about noon. You are in school part of the afternoon. You may work on some afternoons. You eat dinner in the evening. At night you may study or work. You sleep during the night.

When the hours are morning hours, the letters A.M. follow the time. Example: 7:00 A.M. When the hours are afternoon or evening hours, the letters P.M. follow the time. Example: 7:00 P.M.

The letters A.M. and P.M. change at 12:00 midnight and 12:00 noon. The letters A.M. are used after midnight. The letters P.M. are used after 12:00 noon.

You may watch TV at 7:30 P.M. You may eat breakfast at 7:30 A.M.

Read the sentences below. Write A.M. or P.M. in the blank space for each sentence.

1. Sue wakes up each day at 6:30 _____.

2. John rides the school bus home at 3:30 _____.

3. Betty starts her homework at 7:00 _____.

4. George picked up his date at 8:00 _____.

(continued)

Review of Time Concepts (continued)

5. Mary goes to work Saturday morning at 9:00 _____ .

6. The Friday night late show starts at 12:30 _____ .

7. The lunch bell rings at 11:30 _____ .

8. Ralph goes to bed at 10:30 _____ on school nights.

9. Sam delivers morning newspapers at 6:00 _____ .

10. Baseball practice begins at 4:00 _____ after school.

* *

Review of Time Concepts Activity

Part A.

Put these words in the correct order.

night	midnight	noon
dawn	dusk	afternoon
evening	morning	

1. _____   5. _____

2. _____   6. _____

3. _____   7. _____

4. _____   8. _____

(continued)

Review of Time Concepts (continued)

Part B.

Put these times in the correct order. Begin with 1:00 A.M..

3:00 P.M.	5:00 A.M.	11:00 P.M.
4:30 A.M.	7:30 P.M.	5:00 P.M.
1:00 A.M.	6:00 A.M.	10:30 A.M.
2:30 P.M.	8:00 P.M.	9:00 P.M.
12:00 noon	6:30 P.M.	2:00 A.M.
12:00 midnight	1:00 P.M.	11:00 A.M.

1. _____
2. _____
3. _____
4. _____
5. _____
6. _____

7. _____
8. _____
9. _____
10. _____
11. _____
12. _____

13. _____
14. _____
15. _____
16. _____
17. _____
18. _____

Part C.

Place each of these words in the correct box.

sunset	dawn	evening	lunch
school begins	afternoon	breakfast	school ends
morning	dinner	sunrise	homework

dusk

A.M.	P.M.

Review of Time

A clock that shows the hour time has the long hand on the 12. The small hand points to the hour. Like this:

3:00   7:00   1:00   10:00

An hour is 60 minutes long. It takes 60 minutes for the hands to move from 1:00 to 2:00. It takes 60 minutes for the hands to move from 2:00 to 3:00.

Half an hour is 30 minutes long. When the long hand is on the 6, it is 30 minutes past the hour, or half past. Like this:

3:30   7:30   1:30   10:30

The clock can also be divided into quarters. Like this:

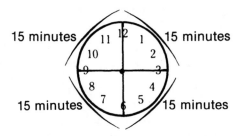

Each quarter is 15 minutes long. When the long hand points to the 3, it is 15 minutes past the hour. Like this:

3:15   7:15   1:15   10:15

(continued)

Review of Time (continued)

When the long hand is on the 9, it shows 15 minutes before the next hour, or 45 minutes past the hour.

3:45   7:45   1:45   10:45

These clocks show time that passes for 1 hour. Write the time of each clock on the line below it.

1.    2.    3.    4.    5.

_____   _____   _____   _____   _____

* *

Review of Time Activity

Part A.

Write the time of each clock below.

1.   2.   3.   4.

_____   _____   _____   _____

5.   6.   7.   8.

_____

(continued)

Review of Time Activity (continued)

Part B.

Draw the hands to show the time on each clock below.

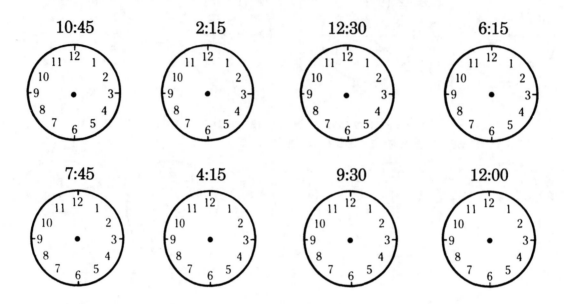

| 10:45 | 2:15 | 12:30 | 6:15 |

| 7:45 | 4:15 | 9:30 | 12:00 |

Review of Minutes

Each hour has 60 minutes. Between every 2 numbers on a clock face, there are 5 minutes.

Look at this clock face. Some minutes are missing. Write the missing minutes where they belong on the clock face.

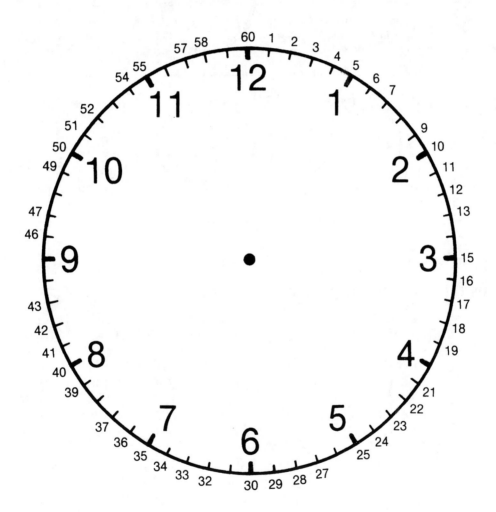

Review of Minutes Activity

Part A.

Write the time of each clock below.

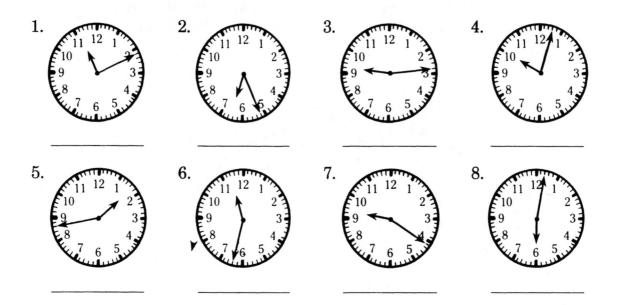

1. _____   2. _____   3. _____   4. _____

5. _____   6. _____   7. _____   8. _____

Part B.

Draw the hands to show the times below.

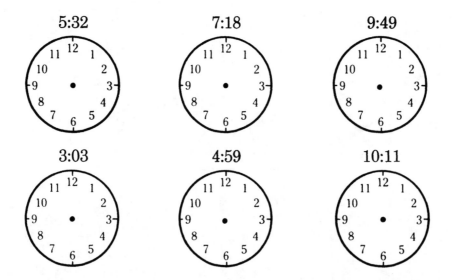

5:32   7:18   9:49

3:03   4:59   10:11

Clock Application

To plan your day you need to know how much time to allow for different things. It may take you 20 minutes to ride the bus or walk to school. You may be in school for 6 or 7 hours. Maybe you have a meeting after school. Or maybe you go to work after school. Help James plan his day. Use the clock face to count the hours and minutes. Write the answers in the blank spaces after the questions.

1. School begins at 8:30 A.M. James walks to school. The walk takes 20 minutes. What time should James leave home?

_____

2. Each class lasts 55 minutes. There are 5 minutes between classes. There are 3 classes before lunch. What time is

   lunch? _____

3. Lunch is 45 minutes long. What time is lunch over?

_____

4. After lunch, James has 5 minutes to walk to his next class. What time does the class start?

_____

5. Each class lasts 55 minutes. There are 5 minutes between classes. James has 3 classes after lunch. What time does the last class begin?

_____

(continued)

Clock Application (continued)

6. At what time is the last class over?

   _____

7. It takes James 10 minutes to walk to work after school. What time does James get to work?

   _____

8. James works for 2 hours and 30 minutes. At what time does James finish work?

   _____

9. It takes James 10 minutes to walk from work to his house. What time does he get home?

   _____

10. James has dinner 20 minutes after he returns home from work. What time does James eat?

    _____

11. James and his family finish dinner at 7:15. James begins his homework. James works on homework for 2 hours. What time does he finish?

    _____

12. James goes to bed 45 minutes after he finishes his homework. What time does James go to bed?

    _____

Clock Application Activity

Draw hands for the times below.

3 hours past 6:30	**20 minutes after 1:45**	**20 minutes before 8:30**
1. 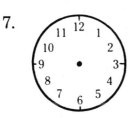	2. 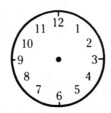	3.

2 hours before 6:15	**1½ hours after 4:20**	**7 hours after 7:30**
4.	5.	6.

1 hour and 45 minutes past 2:15	**4½ hours before 9:30**	**6 hours after 5:15**
7. 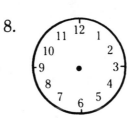	8. 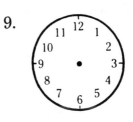	9.

Simple Time Scheduling

You may have many things to do on the weekend. Gary has a busy Saturday. He must do all of the things listed below. Can you plan a time schedule for him? Be sure to write down the time he wakes up, eats meals, and goes to bed. Write the answers in the blank schedule below.

Wash the car – 1 hour
mow the grass – 1½ hours
feed the dog – 5 minutes
clean the bird cage – 20 minutes
take a shower

work at Pizza House – 3:00 P.M. – 6:00 P.M.
get a hair cut – 30 minutes
get ready for date
pick Sue up at 7:30 P.M.
movie ends at 10:00 P.M.

Things to Do	Time
1.	
2.	
3.	
4.	
5.	
6.	
7.	
8.	
9.	
10.	
11.	
12.	
13.	
14.	

(continued)

Simple Time Scheduling (continued)

Pam has a busy weekend also. Plan a schedule for Pam.
Be sure to write the times for waking, eating, dressing, and
going to bed. Write the answers in the blank schedule below.

Ballet lesson – 9:00 A.M.-10:00 A.M.
take Grandmother Shopping–1 hour
pick up dress at cleaners–15 minutes
work at Pizza House–1:00 P.M. to 4:00 P.M.
go to library, return book, check out
another book–30 minutes

Wash car – 1 hour
get ready for basketball game
report to gym –7:00 P.M.
game over – 8:30 P.M.
go to Jane's house after
game – 9:00 P.M.

Things to Do	Time
1.	
2.	
3.	
4.	
5.	
6.	
7.	
8.	
9.	
10.	
11.	
12.	
13.	
14.	

Simple Time Scheduling Activity

Plan the schedules below. Write the things in the correct order.

Ed's Day

Eat lunch, 12:00 noon	Get dressed
Shower, 8:00–8:15 A.M.	Eat breakfast
Wash car, 1 hour	Work, 1:00–5:00 P.M.
Get hair cut	Go to cleaners, 15 minutes
Wake up, 7:30	Baseball practice, 5:30–6:30 P.M.
Eat dinner	Movies, 2 hours
Library, 30 minutes	Homework, 1½ hours

Things to Do	Time
1. _____	_____
2. _____	_____
3. _____	_____
4. _____	_____
5. _____	_____
6. _____	_____
7. _____	_____
8. _____	_____
9. _____	_____
10. _____	_____
11. _____	_____
12. _____	_____
13. _____	_____
14. _____	_____

(continued)

Simple Time Scheduling Activity (continued)

Mary's Day

Eat dinner

Wash hair

Shower

Dress for school

Go to library, 15 minutes

School, 9:00–3:00

Lunch, 12:00–12:30

Wrap present, 10 minutes

Work, 3:30–5:00

Drive home, 20 minutes

Wash dishes, 30 minutes

Buy birthday present for Sam, 30 minutes

Sam's party, 7:00 P.M.

Dress for party

Things to Do	Time
1.	
2.	
3.	
4.	
5.	
6.	
7.	
8.	
9.	
10.	
11.	
12.	
13.	
14.	

Intermediate Time Scheduling

Every spring the students who attend Maymont High School must choose their classes for the next year. Max must choose the right classes and put the classes on his schedule.

He has decided to arrange his schedule this way:

8:30–9:20	English
9:30–10:20	Math
10:30–11:20	Reading
11:30–12:20	Science
12:20–1:00	Lunch
1:10–2:00	History
2:10–3:00	P.E.

Sue needs to select her classes and arrange her schedule. She must take the following classes this year:

Algebra	Science	Art
History	English	Reading

Sue's lunch time is 12:20–1:00. Can you write the classes she must take on a schedule? Here are the times the classes are taught each day:

8:30–9:20	English	10:30–11:20	Writing
8:30–9:20	Math	11:30–12:20	English
8:30–9:20	Science	11:30–12:20	Math
8:30–9:20	Reading	11:30–12:20	Science
9:30–10:20	English	1:10–2:00	History
9:30–10:20	Algebra	1:10–2:00	Math
9:30–10:20	Science	1:10–2:00	P.E.
9:30–10:20	Spelling	2:10–3:00	Art
10:30–11:20	English	2:10–3:00	P.E.
10:30–11:20	Social Studies	2:10–3:00	Band
10:30–11:20	Science		

(continued)

Intermediate Time Scheduling (continued)

Name:____Sue Jones____

Schedule for 10th Grade

8:30–9:20 _____

9:30–10:20 _____

10:30–11:20 _____

11:30–12:20 _____

12:20–1:00 _____

1:10–2:00 _____

2:10–3:00 _____

Intermediate Time Scheduling Activity

George needs to choose the classes he will take next year. He must take the following classes so that he can graduate at the end of next year:

Business Math	Reading
Government	Business Education
Metal Shop II	P.E.
English	

George's lunch is from 12:00 to 12:30. The following classes are offered next year. Choose the classes George needs and write the classes on the schedule on the next page.

8:00–8:50	English	8:00–8:50	History	8:00–8:50	Math
9:00–9:50	English	9:00–9:50	Business Math	9:00–9:50	Science
10:00–10:50	Science	10:00–10:50	Government	10:00–10:50	History
11:00–11:50	Business Ed.	11:00–11:50	Government	11:00–11:50	History
12:30–1:20	P.E.	12:30–1:20	Reading	12:30–1:20	English
1:30–2:20	Art	1:30–2:20	Reading	1:30–2:20	P.E.
2:30–3:20	Art	2:30–3:20	P.E.	2:30–3:20	Metal Shop II

(continued)

Intermediate Time Scheduling Activity (continued)

Name: Georgia Smith

Time	Class
8:00–8:50	_____
9:00–9:50	_____
10:00–10:50	_____
11:00–11:50	_____
12:00–12:30	_____
12:30–1:20	_____
1:30–2:20	_____
2:30–3:20	_____

Complex Time Scheduling

Sometimes you need to plan a week or two ahead. You may have to plan a work schedule or homework schedule for some longer time period. Ben had to plan ahead for both work and school. Ben also had football practice and art lessons. This is what his schedule looked like for one week.

Sunday   2:00–7:00 — Work
           7:00–9:00 — Homework: Science, English,
                       outline Science paper
           10:00 — Bed

Monday   6:30 — Wake/Shower/Dress
           7:30 — Catch school bus
           8:00–3:00 — Classes
           3:00–5:00 — Football practice
           5:30 — Dinner
           6:00–7:00 — Art lesson
           7:00–9:00 — Work
           9:00–10:30 — Homework: Science, Math

Tuesday   Same except no art
           6:00–7:00 — Library: Check out science books

Wednesday 3:00–5:00 — Football practice
           5:30 — Dinner
           6:00–9:00 — Work
           9:00–10:30 — Homework: Math, English,
                       Science

Thursday   3:00–5:00 — Football practice
           5:30 — Dinner
           6:00–8:00 — Work
           8:00–10:30 — Homework: Science term paper,
                       Math

(continued)

Complex Time Scheduling (continued)

Friday   3:00-5:00 — Football practice
            5:30 — Dinner
            7:00 — Football Game
            10:00 — Home, bed

Saturday   8:00-12:00 — Work
            12:30 — Lunch
            1:00-4:00 — Library: work on Science paper
            4:00-5:00 — Write Part I of Science paper
            5:30 — Eat dinner
            6:00 — Shower/Dress
            7:00-11:00 — Out: Movies
            11:30 — Home, bed

Write the answers to the following questions.

1. What time did Ben go to school each day?

_____

2. What day did Ben not go to work?_____

3. What day did Ben have his art lesson?

_____

4. What was Ben's long-term homework project?

_____

_____

5. When did Ben write his outline?_____

6. On what day did Ben check out books from the library?

_____

7. What day did Ben go to work in the morning?

_____

(continued)

Complex Time Scheduling (continued)

8. What night did Ben work on his homework for 2½ hours?

   _____

9. What day did Ben go to work at 2:00 P.M.?

   _____

10. How many days did Ben have football practice?

   _____

* *

Complex Time Scheduling Activity

Help Rachel arrange her schedule for the next week. She must include the following:

1. School: 8:00 A.M. to 3:30 P.M.

2. Piano lesson: Wednesday from 6:30 to 7:30 P.M.

3. Work 6 days for a total of 18 hours (Monday through Friday, hours can be anytime from 4:00 P.M. to 9:00 P.M.; Saturday, hours can be anytime from 8:00 A.M. to 6:00 P.M.)

4. Practice for the school play on Tuesday and Thursday from 3:30 to 4:30.

5. A Government paper is due next Monday. Rachel must (a) go to the library, (b) write an outline, (c) complete a rough draft of the paper, and (d) copy the paper over.

6. Rachel usually has English and Math homework Monday through Thursday.

7. Rachel goes to bed by 10:30 P.M. on school nights.

(continued)

Complex Time Scheduling Activity (continued)

Sunday
_____
_____
_____

Monday
_____
_____
_____

Tuesday
_____
_____
_____

Wednesday
_____
_____
_____

Thursday
_____
_____
_____

Friday
_____
_____
_____

Saturday
_____
_____
_____

Unit III—Measuring

Measuring Inches

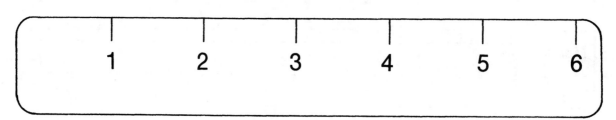

One way to measure things is to use a ruler. Rulers are marked in inches. Each inch is shown by a number.

Read the questions. Write the answers in the blanks.

1. One way to measure things is to use a _____.

2. Rulers are marked in_____.

3. Each inch is shown by a_____.

4. Look at the ruler on this page. This ruler is_____ inches long.

5. A line that is 3 inches long would begin and end where?

_____

6. A 6-inch line would be as long as the

_____.

Measuring Inches Activity

Use your ruler. Measure each line. Write the number of inches for each line on the spaces below.

_____   _____

1. _____ inches   2. _____ inches

3. _____ inches   4. _____ inches

5. _____ inches

6. _____ inches

Measuring to the Half-Inch

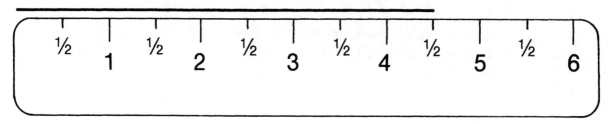

Each number on the ruler shows an inch. Each line that is exactly between 2 numbers shows a half-inch mark.

Read the questions. Write the answers in the blanks.

1. Look at this ruler. This ruler is _____ inches long.

2. Each number shows the number of_____ .

3. Each line between the numbers shows _____ inches.

4. Write the length of the line shown above the ruler.

   _____

5. A line whose length is right between the 5 and the 6 is

   5 and_____ inches long.

6. A line whose length is right between the 2 and the 3 is

   _____ inches long.

7. A line whose length is right between the 3 and the 4 is

   _____ inches long.

8. A line whose length is right between the 1 and the 2 is

   _____ inches long.

Measuring to the Half-Inch Activity

Use your ruler. Measure each line. Write the length of each line in the spaces below.

_____

1. _____ inches

_____

2. _____ inches

_____

3. _____ inches

_____

4. _____ inches

5. _____ inches

6. _____ inches

Measuring to the Quarter-Inch

Each mark that is right between numbers stands for ½ inch. Each mark that is right between a number and a ½ mark stands for ¼ inch.

Read the questions. Write the answers in the blanks.

1. This ruler is_____ inches long.

2. The large numbers 1, 2, 3, 4, 5, and 6 stand for

_____.

3. The mark halfway between the 1 and the 2 measures

_____ an inch.

4. The mark halfway between the 1 and the ½ measures

_____ inch .

5. Count the fourths (¼'s) in each inch. How many fourths

are in each inch?_____

6. How many fourths (¼'s) are there in each ½-inch?

_____

7. The length of a line that is exactly between 4½ and 5

inches is how long?_____

8. The length of a line that is exactly between the 2- and the

2½-inch marks is how long? _____

9. The length of a line that is exactly between the 3½- and

4-inch marks is how long?_____

10. The length of a line that is exactly between the 1½- and

the 2-inch marks is how long?_____

Measuring to the Quarter-Inch Activity

Use your ruler. Measure each line. Write the length of each line in the spaces below.

1. _____ inches

2. _____ inches

3. _____ inches

4. _____ inches

6. _____ inches

5. _____ inches

7. _____ inches

8. _____ inches

Measuring Review

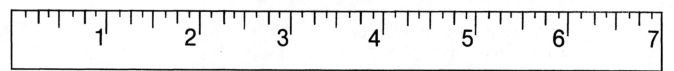

Rulers, like this one, are used every day to measure size. Each ruler has numbers on it to mark the inches.

This ruler is_____ inches long. Between each set of numbers, there are lines. These lines show you parts of the inch.

This line shows you where half of the inch is:

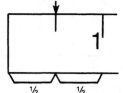

There are 2 halves in each inch.

These lines mark the fourths of the inch:

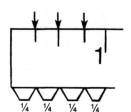

There are 2 fourths in each ½ inch and 4 fourths in each inch. Count the fourths.

These lines mark the eighths of the inch:

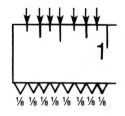

There are 2 eighths in each ¼ inch. There are 4 eighths in each ½ inch. There are 8 eighths in each inch. Count the eighths.

1. How many halves are in 2 inches? _____

2. How many fourths are in 2 inches? _____

3. How many eighths are in 1½ inches? _____

4. How many fourths are in 1½ inches? _____

Measuring Review Activity

Look at this ruler.

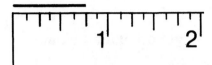

1. How long is the line above the ruler?_____

2. How many eighths are included in the length of the line?

_____

Look at this ruler.

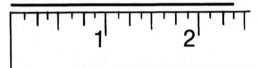

3. How long is the line above the ruler?_____

4. How many eighths are included in the length of the line?

_____

Look at this ruler.

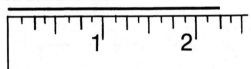

5. How long is the line above the ruler?_____

6. How many fourths are included in the length of the line?

_____

7. How many eighths?_____

Use your ruler to draw 3 inches in the space below. Mark the inches, half-inches, quarter-inches, and eighth-inches.

Measuring with a Ruler

You know that a ruler is divided into inches, half-inches, quarter-inches, and eighth-inches.

The marks on the ruler help you get an exact measure. The sign ″ means inches.

Use your ruler to measure the following shapes. Write the measurements on the lines below the shapes. Remember to write ″ after the numbers.

1. _____*a*_____

   a_____

2.

   a_____

   b_____

   c_____

3.

   a_____

   b_____

   c_____

   d_____

4.

   a_____

   b_____

   c_____

   d_____

(continued)

Measuring with a Ruler (continued)

5. Are all the sides of shape number 2 the same length?

    _____

6. Are all the sides of shape number 3 the same length?

    _____

7. Are all the sides of shape number 4 the same length?

    _____

* *

Measuring with a Ruler Activity

Use your ruler to measure the shapes and lines below.
Write the lengths on the spaces below.

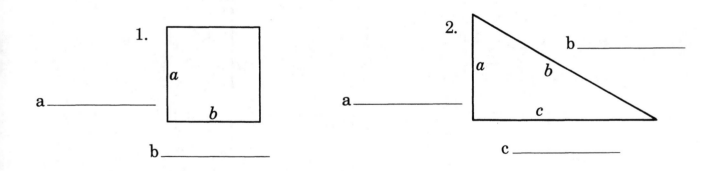

(continued)

Measuring with a Ruler Activity (continued)

Use your ruler to measure the shapes and lines below.
Write the lengths on the spaces below.

3.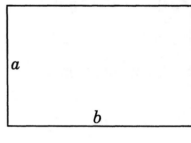

a_____

b_____

4.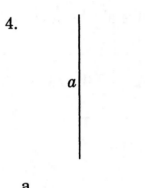

a_____

5. Measure these lines:

_____ a _____

_____ b _____

_____ c _____

Write the lengths on these spaces:

a_____

b_____

c_____

6. Measure these lines:

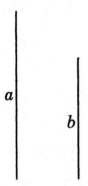

Write the lengths on these spaces:

a_____

b_____

Measuring for Frames

Many times you have a photo or picture you wish to frame. You must be able to measure the picture exactly so the frame will fit.

Look at these photos and pictures below. What are the measurements? Write the answers on the lines below the pictures.

A.

_____

B.

_____

When measurements include length and width, the sign × is placed between the two measurements. A photo that is 3 inches wide and 5 inches long has its measurements written like this:

$$3'' \times 5''$$

Write the correct measurements on the lines above, using the × sign.

Do you have a photo or picture in your class to measure? Write the measurement on the line below.

_____

Measuring for Frames Activity

Use your ruler to measure the following photos and pictures. Write the answers on the spaces below.

1.    2.    3.

_____   _____   _____

Use your ruler to draw frames below for each of the photos. Each frame should be ½″ wide.

Frame 1   Frame 2   Frame 3

Using a Tape Measure

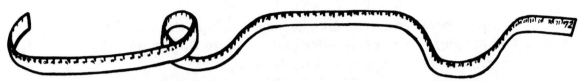

Tape measures are often used to find out length or size. Each tape measure is marked with inches.

This tape measure is_____ inches long.

A tape measure is marked like a ruler. The parts of the inches are marked with lines. Here is a part of a tape measure:

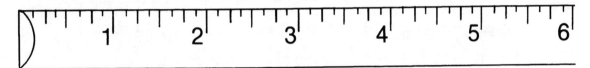

Tape measures can measure many things that are hard to measure with a ruler.

We find the right hat size by measuring the head.

We find the neck size for a shirt by using the tape measure.

We measure the arm with a tape measure to find out the sleeve length.

Use a tape measure to measure: your head, your neck, your arm. Write your measurements on the lines below.

Head: _____ Neck: _____ Arm: _____

Using a Tape Measure Activity

Tape measures are used to measure things that are hard to measure with a ruler. A ruler can measure flat things. A ruler can be used to measure the size of a picture.

To measure things that are not flat, use a tape measure.

Write the answers below.

1. My waist is _____ inches.

2. *(for boys)* My chest is _____ inches.

3. My dress or pants length is

    _____ inches.

4. *(for boys)* My inseam (inside leg) is

    _____ inches long.

5. My wrist is_____ inches.

Other things to measure with a tape measure:

A coffee can _____

A lamp shade _____

Other things in my classroom:

1. _____ is _____ inches.

2. _____ is _____ inches.

3. _____ is _____ inches.

Measuring with a Yardstick

←——————————————— **YARDSTICK** ———————————————→

| 1 | 2 | 3 | 4 | 5 | 6 | 7 | 8 | 9 | 10 | 11 | 12 | 13 | 14 | 15 | 16 | 17 | 18 | 19 | 20 | 21 | 22 | 23 | 24 | 25 | 26 | 27 | 28 | 29 | 30 | 31 | 32 | 33 | 34 | 35 | 36 |

| 1 | 2 | 3 | 4 | 5 | 6 | 7 | 8 | 9 | 10 | 11 | 12 | | 1 | 2 | 3 | 4 | 5 | 6 | 7 | 8 | 9 | 10 | 11 | 12 | | 1 | 2 | 3 | 4 | 5 | 6 | 7 | 8 | 9 | 10 | 11 | 12 |

1 foot = 12 inches　　+　　1 foot = 12 inches　　+ 1 foot = 12 inches = 1 yard

A yardstick is like a long ruler. Most yardsticks are equal to 3 rulers of 1 foot or 12 inches in length. How many feet long is a yardstick? Write the answer on your paper.

Add 12 inches + 12 inches + 12 inches = ——————— inches.

1 foot + 1 foot + 1 foot = ——————— feet.

A yardstick is ——————— inches long or ———————
feet in length.

We use *ft.* to stand for the word *foot* or *feet.*

A yardstick can be used to measure objects that are longer than 1 foot in length. You may need to measure a window for blinds or curtains. You may need to measure the width of a door to see if a large object, like a big table, will fit through the door.

Use a yardstick and measure the width of the door in

your classroom. The door is ——————— inches wide.

If you need to measure a very big thing, such as the height of a door, you use a yardstick. The thing will be longer than the yardstick. You must hold a finger at or mark the place where the yardstick ends. Next, place the yardstick at the marked place to measure the rest of the height.

(continued)

Measuring with a Yardstick (continued)

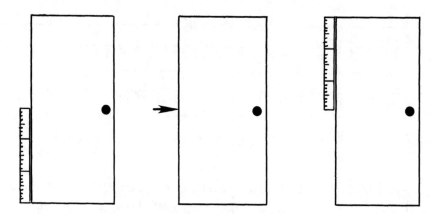

This door is 2 yardsticks tall. If each yardstick equals 36 inches, how many inches tall is the door?

36 inches + 36 inches = _____ inches

The door is 2 yardsticks tall. Each yardstick equals 3 feet. How many feet tall is the door?

3 feet + 3 feet = _____ feet

Measuring with a Yardstick Activity

A yardstick can be used to measure very big objects. A yardstick is used to measure doors, windows, rooms, hallways, and other large areas.

Would curtains made for a window 5 ft. tall and 3 ft. wide fit

this window? _____

What are the measurements of this window?

_____ height (tall)

_____ width (wide)

Measure a window in your classroom or home. Write the measurements here:

_____ height (tall)

_____ width (wide)

Would curtains made for a window 3½ ft. wide and 5½ ft.

tall fit your window? _____

If not, is your window bigger or smaller than the curtains?

_____

(continued)

Measuring with a Yardstick Activity (continued)

Measure the floor of the room you are in now. Write the measurements here:

Floor = _____ by _____

The sign × is used to show the measurements of a flat area instead of the word *by*. Write the floor measurement here:

Floor = _____ × _____

Would a rug that measures 8 ft. by 12 ft. fit in your room?

_____

If not, what size rug would you need?

_____ × _____

If you wanted to leave 1 foot of the floor uncovered, all the way around, what size rug would you need?

_____ × _____

Measuring in the Kitchen

Many things are used to measure when you cook. Most recipes have measurements you need to know.

There are two main kinds of measurement:

1. Dry measures
2. Wet measures

Dry measures are used to measure dry things like salt, sugar, and flour. These are measured by different sizes of spoons and cups when you cook.

Wet measures measure liquid things like milk or water.

Biggest measuring spoon: tablespoon

Next size: teaspoon

Half that size: ½ teaspoon

Half of the half-teaspoon: ¼ teaspoon

Half of the fourth-teaspoon: ⅛ teaspoon

(continued)

Measuring in the Kitchen (continued)

Cups are used to measure dry and wet things, too.

One cup is 8 ounces.

Next size: ½ cup

Next size: ⅓ cup

Next size: ¼ cup

  two ½ cups equal 1 whole cup

   three ⅓ cups equal 1 whole cup

  four ¼ cups equal 1 whole cup

(continued)

Measuring in the Kitchen (continued)

Write the answers to these questions.

1. How many ⅓ cups equal 1 cup?_____

2. Which measuring spoon is the largest? _____

3. Which measuring spoon is next to the smallest?

   _____

4. Which measuring cup is the smallest? _____

* *

Measuring in the Kitchen Activity

Answer the following questions.

1. How many ⅓ cups make a whole cup?_____

2. How many ½ cups make a whole cup? _____

(continued)

Measuring in the Kitchen Activity (continued)

3. How many ¼ cups make a whole cup? _____

4. How many ¼ cups make a half cup? _____

5. If your recipe needs 1¾ cups, which cups could you use?

   _____

6. The largest spoon is called a _____.

7. The next largest spoon is called a _____.

8. How many ¼ teaspoons are in a whole teaspoon?

   _____

9. How many ⅛ teaspoons are in a whole teaspoon?

   _____

10. How many ¼ teaspoons are in ½ teaspoon? _____

11. How many ⅛ teaspoons are in ½ teaspoon? _____

12. How many ⅛ teaspoons are in ¼ teaspoon? _____

Answer the measurement problems below.

1 cup = _____ ½ cups

1 cup = _____ ¼ cups

1 cup = _____ ⅓ cups

½ cup = _____ ¼ cups

1 teaspoon = _____ ½ teaspoons

1 teaspoon = _____ ¼ teaspoons

1 teaspoon = _____ ⅛ teaspoons

½ teaspoon = _____ ¼ teaspoons

½ teaspoon = _____ ⅛ teaspoons

Cooking Simple Recipes

Sometime you may need to fix a simple recipe for yourself. You may need to use kitchen measures to cook. Here are some simple recipes you may want to fix.

Soup is a good and simple food. Here is a fast recipe:

1 can your favorite soup
1 can water
(1 can opener, pan, bowl, cooking spoon, soup spoon)

Open can. Pour soup into pan. Fill empty can with water. Pour water into pan. Heat over medium heat on stove. Stir from time to time. In a few minutes, when soup is warm, spoon into bowl. EAT! Don't forget to turn stove to OFF!

Write the answers to these questions.

1. How much water does the recipe need?_____

_____

2. You should heat over _____ heat.

3. Do you cook in the oven or on the stove?_____

_____

4. The last thing to do is turn _____

_____.

(continued)

Cooking Simple Recipes (continued)

On a cold day or at night before bed, try this recipe!

Instant Cocoa

¾ cup water   1 envelope instant hot cocoa
3 marshmallows
     (measuring cup, pan, coffee mug, spoon)

Measure ¾ cup water. Pour into pan. Heat over medium heat. Empty cocoa mix into coffee mug. When water boils, pour into cup. (Use hot pad to pick up pan.) Stir water and cocoa mix until well blended. Place marshmallows on top and DRINK! Don't forget to turn stove to OFF!

Write the answers to these questions.

1. How much water does the recipe need?_____

   _____

2. What is the second step of the recipe?_____

   _____

3. What do you do with the marshmallows?_____

   _____

4. When is the water ready?_____

   _____

5. What is the last thing you do?_____

   _____

Cooking Simple Recipes Activity

Breakfast Biscuits

2½ cups biscuit mix   ⅔ cup milk
flour
(waxed paper, cookie sheet, glass or biscuit cutter,
rolling pin, large mixing bowl, spoon)

First: Heat oven to 450°.   Makes 10 to 14 biscuits

Wipe counter top clean. In mixing bowl, stir together
biscuit mix and milk. When dough forms, sprinkle
flour on counter (or waxed paper). Roll dough to ½″
thickness. Use glass rim or biscuit cutter to cut biscuits. Place biscuits on cookie sheet. Put in heated
oven. Bake until tops are golden—about 8–10 minutes.
Take out of oven. Turn oven to OFF. EAT biscuits with
butter and honey or jam!

---

1. What is the *first* thing you do?_____

   _____

2. Why should you wipe off the counter?_____

   _____

3. How much biscuit mix do you use?_____

   _____

4. How much milk do you use?_____

   _____

(continued)

Cooking Simple Recipes Activity (continued)

5. What temperature is the oven set for?_____

   _____

6. If you don't have a biscuit cutter, how can you cut the

   biscuits out of the rolled dough?_____

   _____

7. How thick should the dough be?_____

   _____

8. How long do you bake the biscuits?_____

   _____

9. You should remember to_____

   _____ after you take the biscuits out.

10. What do you like to eat on biscuits?_____

    _____

11. How many biscuits will this recipe make?_____

    _____

12. What are some reasons why the recipe might make as

    few as 10 biscuits or as many as 14?_____

    _____

    _____

    _____

Unit IV—Resources

Using the Telephone Book

When you need to find a name in the telephone book, you have to use alphabetical order. The names are listed in the order of the alphabet.

Look at this list. Write the answers to the questions below the list.

Harris	Herndon
Harrison	Hicks
Hart	Hoag
Harvey	Holman
Haskins	Howard
Haynes	Hubbard
Heath	Hughes

1. Between which two names should Hartley be listed?

   _____

2. Which name is alphabetized by using the first and second

   letters only? _____

3. Which two names have the first six letters alike?

   _____

4. Which two *Ha* names are alphabetized by using the third

   letter? _____

5. Between which two names should Hucks be listed?

   _____

(continued)

Using the Telephone Book (continued)

6. Now alphabetize the following names in the space below. Put the first name by the number 1, and so on.

Holland	Towns
Glover	Roberts
Stimpson	Richards
Bauder	Hopkins
Beasley	Wood
Bates	Wise

1. _____   7. _____

2. _____   8. _____

3. _____   9. _____

4. _____   10. _____

5. _____   11. _____

6. _____   12. _____

Using the Telephone Book Activity

Use this list to answer the questions below.

Allen, Tom	Ford, James
Ayers, Sue	Garrett, Mary
Banks, R. J.	Glass, Mark
Brooks, Steven	Jackson, F. B.
Brown, R. S.	Jackson, F. J.
Brown, William	Kelly, Sarah
Clark, Ben	McGee, Marshall
Davis, T. J	Nash, Martha, M.D.
Eastgate Shop	Pine, K. L.

1. Which letters of the alphabet have no names listed between Glass and Jackson?

   _____

2. T. J. Davis is between which two names?

   _____

3. What is used to alphabetize R. S. Brown and William Brown?

   _____

4. Between which two names would you place the name Ralph Morton?

   _____

5. Which name is the name of a store or a business?

   _____

6. Which name is a doctor?

   _____

(continued)

Using the Telephone Book Activity (continued)

7. Which names are alphabetized using the initial for the middle name?

   _____

   _____

8. Place these names in the correct places in the list below:
   Sue Gem,   G. H. Geder,   Maureen Jackson,
   Abel Jackson,   Jake Glower.

   Garrett, Mary

   _____

   _____

   Glass, Mark

   _____

   _____

   Jackson, F. B.
   Jackson, F. J.

   _____

Using the Yellow Pages

You know how to find a name in the phone book. You can also find names of businesses in the same way. The names are in alphabetical order. The stores or businesses are grouped. These groups are in alphabetical order. These groups have titles at the tops of the pages.

Look at these pages. Answer the questions below by filling in the blanks.

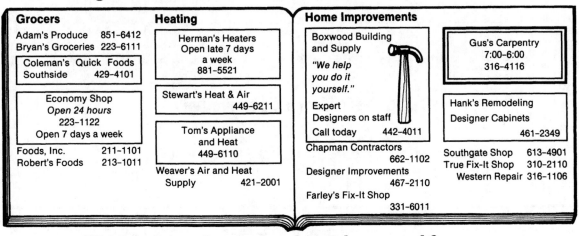

1. Which heating shop is open late 7 days a week?

   _____

2. Which grocery store is open 24 hours?_____

3. Which grocery is located on the South Side?

   _____

4. Which home improvement shop has designer cabinets?

   _____

5. Which home improvement shop has expert designers on

   staff?_____

6. Why are the heating shops listed before the home improvement firms?

   _____

(continued)

Using the Yellow Pages (continued)

7. Between which two heating shops would Robertson's Heating be listed?

_____

8. Which home improvement shop is open from 7:00 A.M. to 6:00 P.M.?

_____

* *

Using the Yellow Pages Activity

Use the Yellow Pages shown here to answer the questions below.

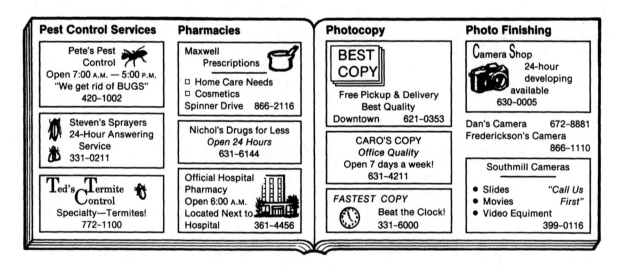

1. Which Pest Control Service is open 24 hours each day?

_____

2. Which Pest Control specializes in termite control?

_____

(continued)

Using the Yellow Pages Activity (continued)

3. Which Photocopy shop is open 7 days a week?

_____

4. Which Pharmacy is located near the hospital?

_____

5. Which Pharmacy is open 24 hours a day?

_____

6. Which Photo Finishing shop has video equipment?

_____

7. Which Pharmacy has home care needs?

_____

8. Which Photocopy shop has free pickup and delivery service?

_____

9. Which Photo Finishing shop has 24-hour developing available?

_____

10. Which Pest Control Service opens at 7:00 A.M?

_____

11. Which Pharmacy is located on Spinner Drive?

_____

12. Which Photocopy shop is located downtown?

_____

Locating Community Services and Emergency Resources

Listed here are some community resources for an imaginary town. Answer the questions below the list.

Be sure that you know the *real* emergency phone numbers for your city or town!

Community Services

Air & Water Pollution
State Control Board 424-6110

Child Abuse
Child Abuse & Neglect Northside 424-1110
Child Abuse & Neglect Southbranch 327-2100

Electric Power Failure
Central Division Cooperative. 721-3100
Northside Electric Cooperative. 424-4617
Western Electric & Power Company. 331-7171

Employment
State Employment Commission 721-6104

Health Care
Central Health Department 721-4888
County Health Services 331-4616
Mental Health Services 721-9669

Hospital
Community Hospital. 331-5555
General City Hospital 721-6010

---

1. If you lived on the north side of town and your electrical power stopped, what number would you call?

_____

2. You need to get information about a job. Whom should you

call?_____

(continued)

Locating Community Services (continued)

3. You think a child in your area is neglected. You live in the south part of town. Which resource should you call?

_____

4. Your school is the middle of town. In a power outage, which number would your principal or teacher call?

_____

5. The river near your home suddenly has lots and lots of dead fish. The water looks funny, too. Whom should you call?

_____

6. You need to have a checkup for school in order to be on the tennis team. Where could you go for help?

_____

7. What are the two hospitals listed in this community?

_____

_____

Locating Community Services
and Emergency Resources Activity

Use the following information about Jack's town to fill in the missing parts of the story. (Remember not to use these numbers in a *real* emergency!)

Air & Water Pollution Agency	638-1211
Animal Control	492-6000
Child Abuse & Neglect	471-6133
Electric Power Failure	781-6666
Fire Department	781-5000
Health Care—Ambulance	471-6444
Hospital	360-0100
Library	471-5222
Mental Health	638-0000
Newspaper	492-8111
Post Office	492-6010
Radio Station	360-7731
School	822-9910

One morning Jack woke up. He looked out of his window and saw a big, black, thick cloud above the house next door.

"Oh, no!" he said. "It's a fire! I'll dial _____ to report it!"

Jack ran to the phone—but he tripped. He fell and thought he had broken his leg.

(continued)

Locating Community Services Activity (continued)

"Oh, no!" Jack said. "I'll have to call an _____ !"
The number is _____ .

Jack crawled to the phone. Just then his mother
walked in.

"Oh, no!" she said. "He's lost his head! A 16-year-old
crawling on the floor! I'll call mental health." The number is

_____ .

"Wait!" Jack said. "It's not my head!"

"Well, what is it then?" Jack's mother asked.

"The fire next door—I fell—it's my leg!" said Jack.

"Oh, no!" she said. "It is his head! There's no fire. I'll call
the newspaper to find out for certain." The number is

_____ .

"No fire? What is it, then?" asked Jack.

"I'll be right back," said Jack's mother. When she
returned she said, "The cloud you see is dirty air. It's from
the factory."

"I'll call _____ to report it to the

_____."

"Okay. Now, what's wrong with your leg?" asked Jack's
mom.

(continued)

Locating Community Services Activity (continued)

"I think it's okay. But I'll be late to school," answered Jack.

"I'll call the _____," his mother said. The number is _____.

So Jack went to school late that day, and on the way he saw a funny-looking dog running all over the street. So when he got to school, he called _____. The number is _____.

Unit V—Map Reading

Beginning Map Reading

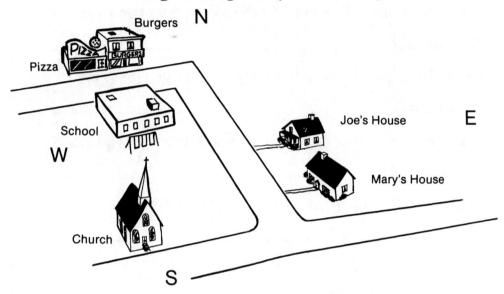

Look at the map. Read the questions. Write the answers in the blanks.

1. Is the pizza shop north or south of the school?

   _____

2. Is the pizza shop north or south of the church?

   _____

3. Is the school north or south of the pizza shop?

   _____

4. Is the school north or south of the church?

   _____

5. Is the church north or south of the school?

   _____

(continued)

Beginning Map Reading (continued)

6. From the church, in which direction must you go to get to Mary's house? _____

7. From the church, in which direction must you go to get to Joe's house? _____

8. From the school, in which direction must you go to get to Joe's house? _____

9. From Mary's house, in which direction must you go to get to the school? _____

10. From the pizza shop, in which direction must you go to get to Mary's house? _____

Beginning Map Reading Activity

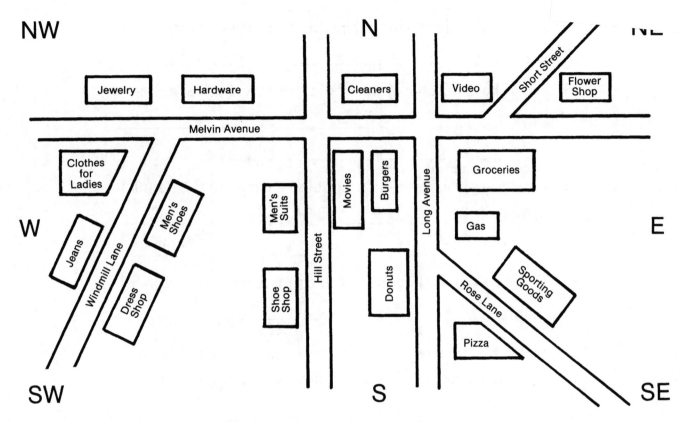

Look at the map. Answer the questions below.

1. Melvin Avenue runs in which direction?_____

2. Hill Street runs in which direction? _____

3. Long Avenue runs in which direction?_____

4. In which direction must you turn to get onto Short Street if you are traveling east on Melvin Avenue?_____

5. Traveling west on Melvin Avenue, you must turn _____ to get onto Windmill Lane.

6. Traveling south on Long Avenue, you must turn in which direction to get onto Rose Lane? _____

(continued)

Beginning Map Reading Activity (continued)

7. If you are at the cleaners, the dress shop is in which direction?_____

8. From the dress shop, how would you travel to the video store?_____

_____

9. From the video store, how would you travel to the donut shop?_____

_____

10. From the donut shop, how would you travel to the jewelry shop?_____

_____

11. Write the directions from the jeans shop to the pizza shop.

_____

_____

12. James is a new student in your town. In the space below, draw a simple map for him. He wants to go from the hardware shop to the sporting goods store.

Reading a School Map

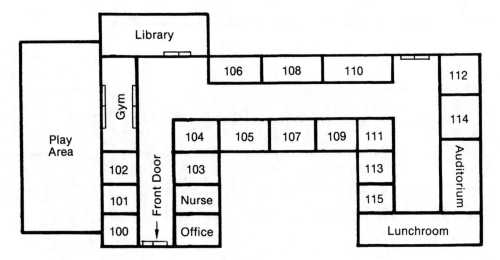

John's little sister Kristy will begin school this year. John knows that:

> Kristy's homeroom teacher will be Mrs. Rogers, room 108.
> Kristy will have art in room 114.
> She will go to music in room 102.
> Kristy will eat lunch in the lunchroom every day.
> She will have P.E. in the gym and on the play area outside.

Help John give his sister directions. In the blanks below, write the following directions:

1. Tell Kristy how to go to Mrs. Rogers's class from the front door. _____

_____

2. Tell Kristy where the office and nurse are as she enters the front door. _____

_____

_____

(continued)

Reading a School Map (continued)

3. Explain how to travel from room 108 to art class.

   _____

   _____

4. Explain how to travel from room 108 to the lunchroom.

   _____

   _____

5. Explain how to travel from room 108 to the music class.

   _____

   _____

6. Tell Kristy how to travel from room 108 to the gym.

   _____

   _____

7. Tell Kristy where the play area is located.

   _____

   _____

8. Tell Kristy how to travel from the front door to the

   auditorium. _____

   _____

9. Tell Kristy how to travel from the lunchroom to her art

   class. _____

   _____

   _____

(continued)

Reading a School Map (continued)

10. Tell Kristy how to travel from the art room to the music

    room. _____

    _____

11. Tell Kristy how to go to the library from the front door.

    _____

    _____

12. Explain how to travel from the library to Mrs. Rogers's

    class. _____

    _____

13. Explain how to go from the library to the lunchroom.

    _____

    _____

14. Explain how to travel from the library to the art room.

    _____

    _____

Reading a School Map Activity

Look at the map. Read the Key. Read Bob's Schedule.

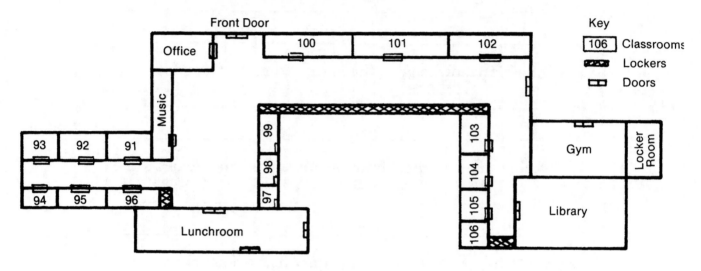

Bob's Schedule		
Period	**Class**	**Room**
1	English	106
2	Math	99
3	History	95
	Lunch	
4	Science	104
5	P.E.	Gym
6	Art	100

Read the following and then answer the questions.

Bob's bus drops him off at the front door each day by the office. Bob's locker is between room 106 and the library. Bob keeps his books for English, math, history, and science in his locker. He keeps his P.E. shorts in the gym locker room.

(continued)

Reading a School Map Activity (continued)

1. When Bob gets to school, he walks in the front door.
   Which way would he turn to go to his locker?

   _____

2. At his locker, Bob gets his _____ book for
   1st period.

3. After 1st period, where does Bob need to go?

   _____

   _____

4. Where is Bob's 2nd period class? _____

   _____

5. Where is Bob's 3rd period class? _____

   _____

6. Bob has only 5 minutes to go from one class to the next.
   To save time, what books can he get from his locker

   after 1st period?_____

   _____

7. After 3rd period, where does Bob go next?

   _____

   _____

8. On the days that Bob brings his lunch from home, he

   would save time if he got his lunch after_____
   period.

9. After lunch, Bob has_____.

(continued)

Reading a School Map Activity (continued)

10. What room is Bob's 4th period class in? _____

11. When Bob leaves the lunch room, he must get his

    _____ book.

12. From the lunch room, write the way that Bob must travel

    inside the school. _____

    _____

13. What does Bob have during 5th period? _____

14. Where is Bob's 5th period class? _____

    _____

15. Before 5th period, Bob returns his books to his locker.
    Which way will he turn to go to his locker?

    _____

16. What class does Bob have last? _____

17. How will Bob travel from 5th to 6th period inside the

    building? _____

    _____

18. After 6th period, Bob must return to his locker. Then Bob
    will go to the bus parked by the front door. How will he
    travel from 6th period to his locker and then to the bus?

    _____

    _____

    _____

    _____

    _____

    _____

Reading Building Maps

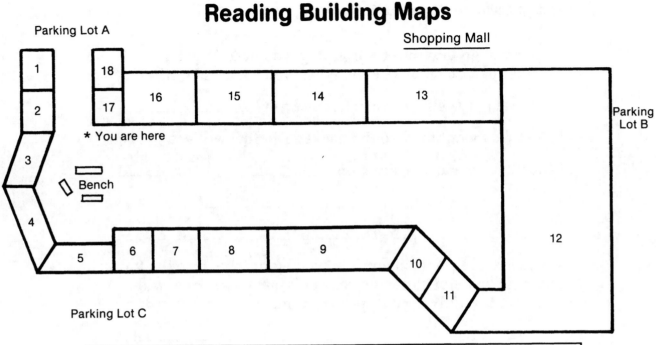

Key

1. Rose's Hair Salon
2. Jeff's Jeans
3. Sharon's Shoes
4. Office Supply
5. Martin's Drugstore
6. Restrooms
7. Helen's Dresses
8. Jake's Bicycles
9. Five and Dime Store
10. Candy & Things
11. Movie III
12. Major's Department Store
13. Ralph's Bookstore
14. Jewelry Plus
15. Frank's Clothier
16. Jason's Sporting Goods
17. Toys by Kristy
18. Carolyn's Plants

Answer these questions.

1. The * shows where you are standing when you look at this map. If you just came in and passed the hair salon, which parking lot did you come from? _____

2. You are facing the bench. Is the office supply on your left or right? _____

(continued)

Reading Building Maps (continued)

3. After you go into the office supply, you need to get a bicycle part to repair a bike. When you come out of the office supply, will you turn left or right? _____

4. Next, you want to go to the bookstore. How will you get there? Write out the directions. _____

_____

_____

5. When you leave the bookstore, you want to go into the toy store to buy a birthday present for your sister. How will you get there? Write out the directions.

_____

_____

6. When you leave the toy store, you will go to Major's Department Store. Write the directions.

_____

_____

7. After you go to Major's, you need to go into the dimestore to buy school supplies. Write the directions.

_____

_____

8. When you leave the dimestore, you need to return to Parking Lot A. Write the directions.

_____

_____

Reading Building Maps Activity

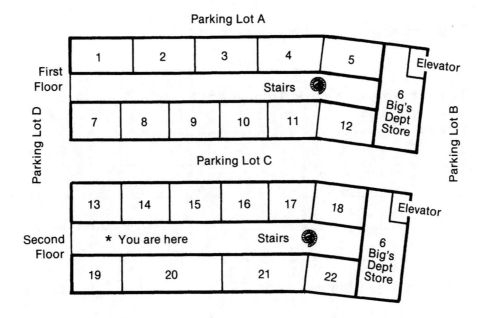

Key

1. Bob's Sporting Goods
2. Shoes & Handbags
3. Toy Shop
4. World Gift Shop
5. Hobbies for Everyone
6. Big's Department Store
7. Darlene's Dresses
8. Men's Shoe Shop
9. Eyeglass Shop
10. Camera Shop
11. Restrooms

12. Children's Shoe Shop
13. Men's Suits
14. Art & Things
15. Children's Clothing Shop
16. Joe's Drugstore
17. Restrooms
18. Hamburgers
19. Bookstore
20. Party Shop
21. Jewelry
22. Bank

1. Which store has 2 floors? _____

2. What is the number of the store with 2 floors?_____

3. The restrooms on the 2nd floor are between which 2

   shops? _____ and _____

(continued)

Reading Building Maps Activity (continued)

4. In which store is an elevator located?

   _____

5. To walk from Bob's Sporting Goods to Joe's Drugstore,

   you would _____

   _____

   _____

   _____ (write directions).

6. The bookstore is located on the _____ floor.

7. The Eyeglass Shop is on the _____ floor.

8. In order to go out to Parking Lot B, you must walk

   through _____

   _____

Small-Town Maps

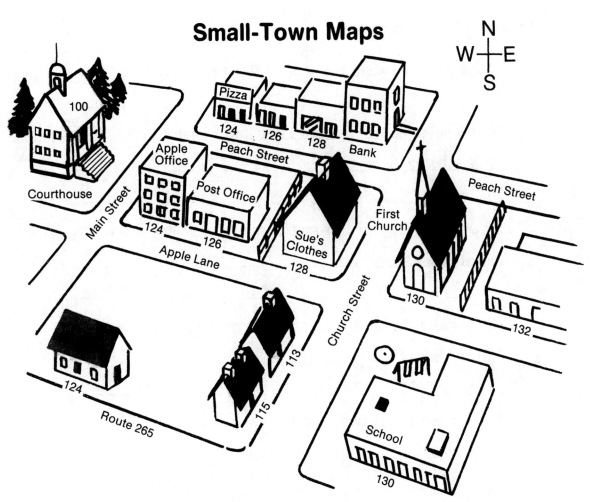

Study the map. Answer the questions in the blanks below.

1. What is the address of the pizza parlor?

   _____

2. What is the address of the First Church?

   _____

3. Is Apple Lane north or south of Route 265?

   _____

4. Is Apple Lane north or south of Peach Street?

   _____

(continued)

Small-Town Maps (continued)

5. Is the courthouse east or west of the post office?

_____

6. How would you travel from 115 Church Street to the

   pizza parlor? _____

   _____

7. How would you travel from the school on Route 265 to the

   courthouse? _____

   _____

8. How would you travel from the courthouse to the bank on

   Church Street? _____

   _____

9. How would you travel from the bank to number 124 on

   Route 265? _____

   _____

10. How would you travel from number 124 on Route 265 to
    First Church on the corner of Apple Lane and Church

    Street? _____

    _____

11. Write the addresses of the Apple Office Building, the post

    office, and Sue's Clothes Shop. _____

    _____

12. What do you see about these addresses on Apple Lane?

    _____

    _____

Small-Town Maps Activity

Look at the map.

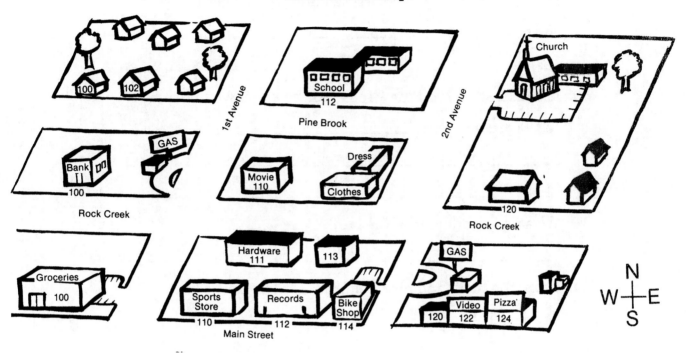

Answer the questions below.

1. Is Pine Brook north or south of Main Street? _____

2. Is Rock Creek north or south of Main Street? _____

3. Is 1st Avenue east or west of 2nd Avenue? _____

4. What is on the corner of Main Street and 1st Avenue?

   _____

5. What is the address of the record shop?

   _____

6. What is the address of the school?

   _____

7. What is the address of the video store?

   _____

(continued)

Small-Town Maps Activity (continued)

8. If you are in the video store, tell how you would travel to

   the school: _____

   _____

9. If you lived at 100 Pine Brook, tell how you would travel

   to the pizza shop: _____

   _____

   _____

10. What is the address of the bank?

   _____

11. From the bank, tell how you would travel to the bike

   shop: _____

   _____

12. What is the address of the hardware store?

   _____

13. The addresses on the south side of Rock Creek are

   _____ numbers.

14. The addresses on the north side of Rock Creek are

   _____ numbers.

15. Do the addresses on Rock Creek get larger or smaller as

   you travel east? _____

Neighborhood Maps

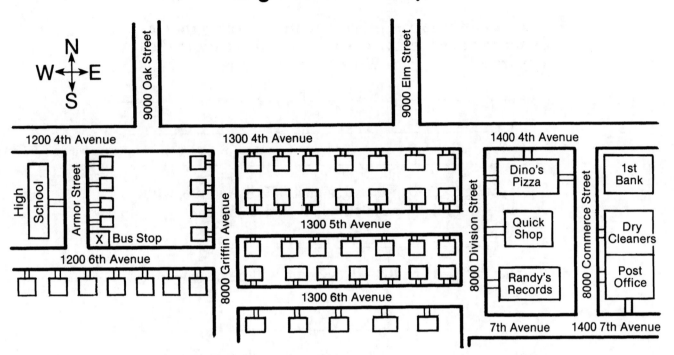

Look at this neighborhood map and answer the following questions. Write the answers in the blanks.

1. The high school is on what street? _____

2. Walking from the school on 6th Avenue, how many blocks

   is it to the Quick Shop? _____

3. Even though you can't see north of 4th Avenue on this map, what do you think the name of the next street will be?

   _____

4. The post office is on what street? _____

5. If you walked out of Dino's Pizza and you wanted to go to the post office, in what direction would you walk? Write

   your directions. _____

   _____

   _____

(continued)

Neighborhood Maps (continued)

6. After leaving the post office, you walk to the corner of Commerce and 7th Avenue. How would you get to the bus stop from that corner? Write your directions.

   _____

   _____

   _____

7. Even though you cannot see south of 7th Avenue, what do you think the name of the next street will be?

   _____

8. A house located at 1401 4th Avenue will be near what business?

   _____

9. It is_____ blocks from 4th Avenue to 7th Avenue.

10. Are there any houses with addresses on the 8000 block of

    Division Street?_____

Neighborhood Maps Activity

1. The elementary school is _____ of the high school and middle school.

2. What street divides Overton Park?_____

3. The high school is located in which block of Orange Street?

   _____

4. How many blocks are between the post office and the

   shopping center?_____

5. How many blocks would you need to walk on Orange Street in order to go from the elementary school to the

   shopping mall?_____

6. Orange Street is 2 blocks_____ of Price.

7. What street is between 6th Street and Frankford?

   _____

8. _____ is 3 blocks east of 1st Street.

(continued)

Neighborhood Maps Activity (continued)

9. Walking from the post office on Price, in which direction is the elementary school?_____

10. If you are in the 1500 block of Sandford, in which direction is the elementary school?_____

11. If you are in the 1500 block of Sandford, in which direction is the high school?_____

12. You need to walk from the bank to the high school. Write down the directions you would follow.

    _____

    _____

    _____

    _____

Simple Road Maps

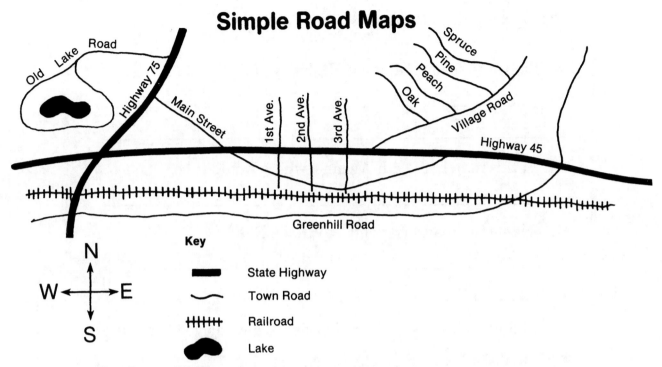

Study the map. Look at the key. Read the questions. Write the answers in the blanks.

1. What does the key tell you? _____

   _____

2. Does Highway 45 run north and south or east and west?

   _____

3. Do the avenues run north and south or east and west?

   _____

4. If you lived on Pine Street, how would you travel to go to

   Highway 45? _____

   _____

5. From Main Street at Highway 45, how would you travel to

   Old Lake Road? _____

   _____

(continued)

Simple Road Maps (continued)

6. Name the roads that cross Highway 45. _____

   _____

   _____

7. If this map had a 4th Avenue, where would it be?

   _____

8. Name the roads that end at Village Road.

   _____

   _____

9. If a new street were named Cedar, where do you think it would be? _____

   _____

10. How would you travel from Old Lake Road to Village Road? _____

    _____

11. From Old Lake Road, how would you travel to Greenhill Road? _____

    _____

12. Name the roads that cross the railroad. _____

    _____

13. Does the railroad run north and south or east and west?

    _____

14. Which road runs east and west, then turns to run north and south? _____

Simple Road Maps Activity

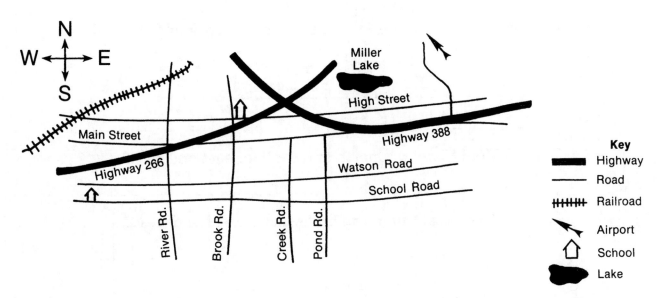

Look at the map. Read the key. Answer the questions below.

1. The schools are on which streets? _____

_____ and _____

2. Is Brook Road east or west of Pond Road?

_____

3. Is Brook Road east or west of River Road?

_____

4. How many blocks apart are River Road and Pond Road?

_____

5. How would you travel from the corner of Pond and School Roads to High Street and River Road?

_____

_____

_____

(continued)

Simple Road Maps Activity (continued)

6. How would you travel from the corner of Brook and
   School Roads to the airport? _____
   _____
   _____

7. Does Main Street run north and south or east and west?
   _____

8. Does River Road run north and south or east and west?
   _____

9. The railroad crosses which streets? _____
   _____

10. Both schools are near which highway? _____
    _____

11. Is the airport east or west of Miller Lake?
    _____

12. Use your pencil to draw the route from the corner of
    Watson and River Roads to the airport.

Detailed Road Maps

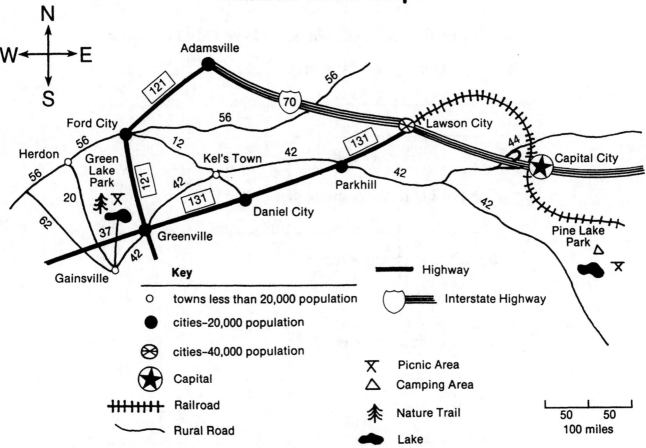

Look at the map. Answer the questions below.

1. If you leave Parkhill and drive east on 42, what must you

   do in order to reach Interstate 70? _____

   _____

   _____

2. If you are in Greenville and you want to drive to Green
   Lake Park, what route would you take?

   _____

   _____

   _____

(continued)

Detailed Road Maps (continued)

3. Write a route that will take you from Ford City to Capital City without going to Adamsville._____

_____

_____

_____

4. In which park can you camp overnight?

_____

5. Which park has a nature trail?

_____

6. About how far do you think it is to travel from Greenville to Daniel City on Highway 131?

_____

7. The railroad goes north from Capital City to what city?

_____

8. Which towns have a population less than 20,000?

_____

_____

_____

_____

Detailed Road Maps Activity

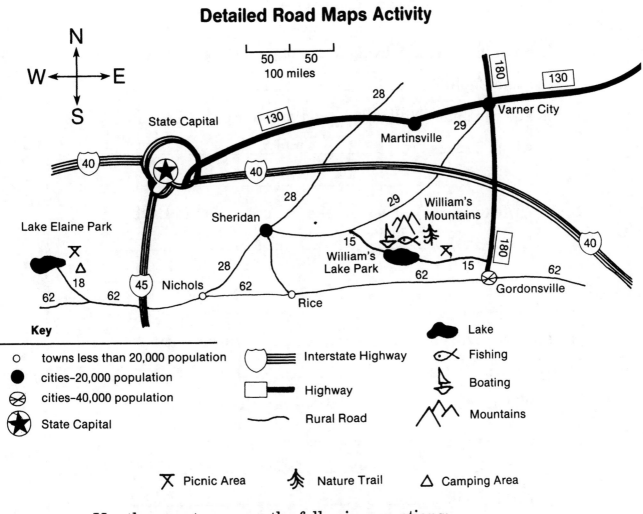

Use the map to answer the following questions:

1. In which park can you camp overnight?

_____

2. Which park has boating and fishing?

_____

3. Write the route you would travel from Varner City to

Sheridan. _____

_____

_____

(continued)

Detailed Road Maps Activity (continued)

4. What interstate highway does not go farther north than State Capital?_____

5. You can get to William's Lake Park on Route 15 from which 2 roads?_____

_____

6. Write the route you would take from Sheridan to Lake Elaine Park._____

_____

_____

7. Martinsville is_____ of Varner City.

8. Varner City is_____ of Gordonsville.

9. Which 2 towns have populations less than 20,000?

_____

10. Write the route you would take from the capital to Gordonsville._____

_____

_____

11. Write the route you would travel from Lake Elaine Park to Varner City. _____

_____

_____

12. About how far is it from Sheridan to Rice?

_____

Unit VI—Problem-Solving

Planning a Party

Read the story. Answer the questions below.

Rick and Beth want to have a party. It is the end of school. They want to have a party on the first day of summer. They want to have things to eat and drink. They want to have music. They want all of the kids in their class to come to the party. There are 20 other kids in their class. They have 3 weeks of school left.

1. What do Beth and Rick want to do?_____

   _____

2. When do they want to do this?_____

   _____

3. How long do they have to plan? _____

   _____

4. How many people will they ask to the party?

   _____

5. If everyone in the class comes to the party, how many will

   be at the party?_____

(continued)

Planning a Party (continued)

6. What do Rick and Beth want to do at the party?

_____

_____

_____

7. Can you think of some good things to eat at the party?

_____

_____

_____

8. What do you think Beth and Rick should do first to plan

   for the party?_____

_____

_____

* *

Planning a Party Activity

Beth and Rick have a lot to do to plan for the party. What do you think they should do first? Draw a line under the answer.

    1. Buy the food.

    2. Invite the class.

    3. Find a place to have the party.

Rick and Beth decide the first thing to do is to find a good place for the party. Help them pick the best place from these choices:

(continued)

Planning a Party Activity (continued)

1. Beth's house. Her den can hold about 15 people. There is no place for dancing.

2. The Town Recreation Center has a free room. This room will hold 40 people. It has a sink and a refrigerator. There is room for dancing.

3. Rick's garage has been changed to a recreation room. It will hold about 20 people. It has a table tennis game in the middle of the room.

4. Beth's church has a Teen Room in the basement. It will hold about 30 people. The refrigerator is in the room next door.

Which place would you pick? _____

_____

Beth and Rick have picked the Town Recreation Center. What should they do next? Draw a line under the answer.

1. Buy the food.

2. Look for recipes.

3. Buy the invitations.

4. Find out who can come to the party.

Rick and Beth talk about the party. They think it is best to find out how many are coming and then buy the food.

Why is this a good idea?_____

_____

How can Rick and Beth find out who is coming to the party? Beth tells Rick that the kids can call her at her house to let her know if they will come. She tells Rick that they can write her phone number on the invitations. Next thing to do: Buy the invitations.

Buying for a Party

Rick and Beth have picked this invitation for the party:

The party is on June 5 from 4:00 P.M. until 8:00 P.M. Beth's phone number is 492-3000.

The inside of the invitation looks like this:

It's A Party!!!

By _____

Date _____

Time _____

Place _____

To Celebrate _____

R.S.V.P. _____

Read the questions. Write the answers in the blanks below.

1. Who is having the party?_____

_____

2. Where will Rick and Beth write their names inside?

_____

(continued)

Buying for a Party (continued)

3. What will be written on the Date line?_____

   _____

4. What time will the party be?_____

   _____

5. Where will the party be held?_____

   _____

6. What will Beth and Rick be celebrating?_____

   _____

7. What is written on the R.S.V.P. line?_____

   _____

8. Beth and Rick like this invitation, but there are only 8 invitations in each package. If they want to invite 20 people, how many packages must they buy?

   _____

9. Each package costs $2.50. Will Rick and Beth be able to buy enough packages with $10.00?_____

   _____

Buying for a Party Activity

1. Rick and Beth sent the invitations. Beth had phone calls from everyone in her class. Of the 20 invited, 18 said they could come to the party. How many will be at the party

   altogether?_____

2. Beth and Rick need to buy other things for the party. One thing they need to buy is a tablecloth. They measured the table at the Town Recreation Center. The table was 72″ long and 36″ wide. Tablecloths are sold in the following sizes. Which one should Rick and Beth buy? Draw a line under the answer.

   a. 48″ × 24″   c. 84″ × 42″

   b. 62″ × 36″   d. 110″ × 52″

3. Rick and Beth want to buy napkins, cups, and plates. Party napkins are sold in packages of 24. How many

   packages will Beth and Rick need to buy?_____

4. Cups are sold 10 to a package. How many packages will

   Rick and Beth need?_____

5. Plates are sold in packages of 12. How many packages will

   Beth and Rick need?_____

6. Rick and Beth have to pick out the food for the party. Here are some of their ideas. Which ones do you like? Circle them.

   onion dip and chips—serves 12

   cheese and crackers

   party mix with nuts—serves 16–20

   cookies—recipe makes 4 dozen

   punch—makes 36 8-oz. cups

(continued)

Buying for a Party Activity (continued)

7. Can you think of other foods? Write them here.

   _____

   _____

   _____

   _____

   _____

8. Of the foods listed by Rick and Beth, which ones will be enough for all of the people at the party?

   _____

   _____

   _____

9. If Beth and Rick want to make the onion dip, how many recipes or "batches" will they need to make?

   _____

10. If a package of cheese serves 10 people, how many packages should Rick and Beth buy?

    _____

Cooking for a Party

Read the following. Then answer the questions in the blanks below.

Beth and Rick decided to have these foods at their party:

onion dip   chips
peanut butter cookies   fruit punch

The onion dip recipe is:

1½ cups of sour cream
2 tablespoons of dry onion soup mix

Mix well together. Chill for 30 minutes before serving.

1. This recipe makes enough for 12 people. What should Rick and Beth do to be sure they have enough dip for 20 people?

   _____

2. Right! They should double the recipe. How much sour cream will they need for a double recipe?

   _____

3. How much dry onion soup mix will they need for a double recipe? _____

4. Each bag of chips serves 8 people. How many bags of chips will Beth and Rick need to buy?

   _____

5. To be sure the dip has chilled in the refrigerator for 30 minutes, what time should Rick and Beth put it in?

   _____

6. What time should they mix the dip?

   _____

Cooking for a Party Activity

Rick and Beth like this recipe for cookies:

½ cup margarine
½ cup sugar
½ cup brown sugar
¾ cup chunky peanut butter
1 egg
½ tsp vanilla
1¼ cups sifted flour
¾ tsp baking soda
¼ tsp salt

Cream together first 6 ingredients in a large bowl. Sift dry ingredients together, then mix with peanut butter mixture. Shape into balls about 1″ in size. Place balls 2″ apart on a cookie sheet. Bake at 375° for 10–12 minutes. Makes 4 dozen.

Beth and Rick can get 16 cookies on each cookie sheet. It will take 3 cookie sheets to bake all 4 dozen cookies. Because the oven will hold only 2 cookie sheets at a time, Rick and Beth must plan time to cook twice. This means they will be baking twice as long.

1. How many minutes will it take Beth and Rick to bake all

   of the cookies?_____

2. If it will take 15 minutes to mix all of the ingredients and 10 minutes to shape the cookies, how long will it take Rick and Beth to get the cookies ready to bake?

   _____

(continued)

Cooking for a Party Activity (continued)

3. To be sure that Beth and Rick have enough time to bake the cookies before the party, they should start making the cookies at what time? Draw a line under your answer.

   3:15 P.M.   3:45 P.M.   2:00 P.M.   3:30 P.M.

4. What temperature should the oven be set to?

   _____

5. List the first 6 ingredients, which should be mixed in the bowl first:

   1. _____

   2. _____

   3. _____

   4. _____

   5. _____

   6. _____

6. What must you do with the dry ingredients?

   _____

   _____

   _____

   _____

   _____

Planning a Trip

Gail and Donna are planning a trip this summer. They are going to a small town near the ocean. The following phone numbers and addresses are ones they may need.

Ocean Tourist Information . .	P.O. Box 201, Oceanside	638–2116
State Forestry Department . .	P.O. Box 2261, PineBrook	782–0031
State Highway Department . .	P.O. Box 4116, PineBrook	782–0061
State Tourist Information . . .	112 Rambling Road, Oak City . .	788–3001
State Weather Bureau	642 Cloud Lane, Windy City . . .	822–6145

Read the questions. Write your answers in the blanks below.

1. Which number or address would Gail and Donna need to find out about camping in the woods on the way to the

   ocean? _____

   _____

2. Which number or address would help them find out about

   highway maps?_____

   _____

3. Which number or address would help them find out about

   places to see in the state?_____

   _____

4. Which number or address would Gail and Donna use to find out about hotels and restaurants near the ocean?

   _____

   _____

(continued)

Planning a Trip (continued)

5. Which number would they use to find out about road conditions the day they start their trip?_____

_____

6. Which number or address would they use to ask for a map of the town near the ocean?_____

_____

7. Which number would they use to find out about the weather the day they start their trip?_____

_____

8. What telephone numbers or addresses would you need to go on a trip in your state?_____

_____

_____

_____

_____

_____

_____

_____

Planning a Trip Activity

Gail and Donna are talking about their trip. They want to leave the morning of July 10. They will leave Mountainside City at 8:00 A.M. After driving 4 hours, they will stop at Pine State Park for a picnic lunch. They plan to leave the park at 1:00 P.M. and drive 4 more hours. They will arrive at Oceanside Village at 5:00 P.M.

Look at the map. Read the questions and answer them below.

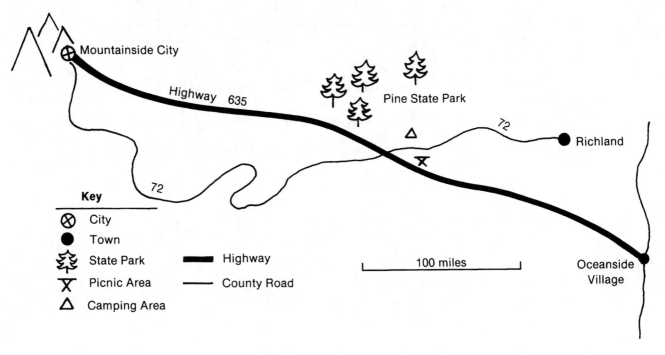

1. What highway runs from Mountainside City to Oceanside Village? _____

2. What other road could Gail and Donna travel on to reach Pine State Park? _____

3. Which is larger, Mountainside or Oceanside?

_____

(continued)

Planning a Trip Activity (continued)

4. Will Gail and Donna be able to picnic at Pine State Park?

   _____

5. What else can people do at the park? _____

   _____

   _____

   _____

   _____

   _____

6. About how far is Mountainside from Pine State Park?

   _____

7. How far do you think Pine State Park is from Oceanside?

   _____

On the Trip

Read the list below. These are things that Gail and
Donna want to do on their trip. The times are given for each.

Marine Museum, Mon.–Sat., 9:00 A.M.–5:30 P.M.

Oceanside Boat Ride, Mon.–Sat., Every half hour,
8:30 A.M.–4:30 P.M.

Oceanside Ferry to Pelican Island leaves every hour,
every day, 9:00 A.M.–3:00 P.M.

Pier for Fishing—Open 5:30 A.M.–7:00 P.M.

Gail and Donna called the Oceanside Ferry for more
information. The ferry takes 1 hour to get to the island. Once
on the island, there is a marine show that lasts for an hour.
Then Gail and Donna would ride the ferry an hour to get back
to Oceanside. The Oceanside Boat Ride lasts 30 minutes.

Read the questions. Write the answers in the blanks below.

1. How many hours will Gail and Donna need to plan for the

   ferry ride?_____

2. If Gail and Donna leave on the 9:00 A.M. ferry, what time

   would they return to Oceanside?_____

3. Would Gail and Donna be able to go to the museum on the

   same morning as they ride the ferry?_____

4. Write a schedule for Gail and Donna. Be sure they are able
   to do all 4 things on the list.

   _____

   _____

   _____

   _____

   _____

On the Trip Activity

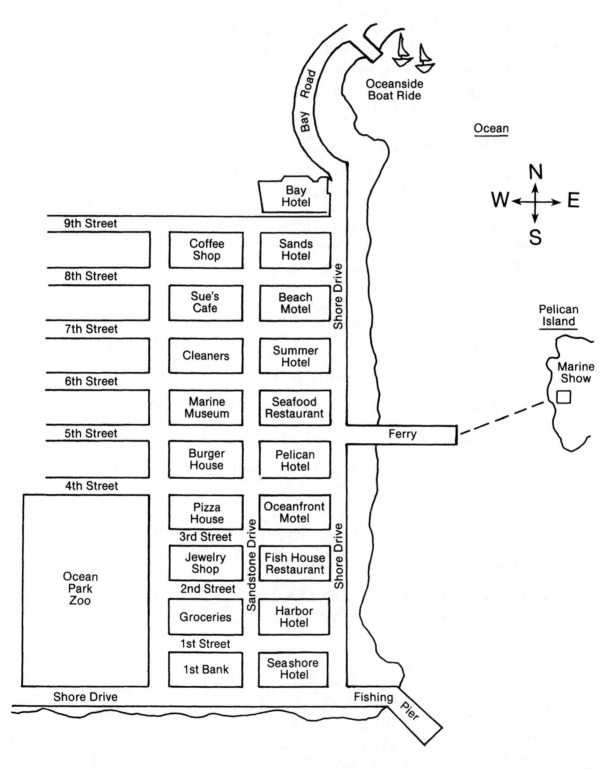

(continued)

On the Trip Activity (continued)

Look at the map on page 134. Answer the questions below.

1. Gail and Donna are staying at the Beach Motel. What streets are around the motel?_____

   _____

   _____

   _____

2. From the Beach Motel, write the way Donna and Gail would travel to the ferry. _____

   _____

   _____

3. From the ferry on Shore Drive, which direction is Pelican Island?_____

   _____

4. From the ferry, how would Gail and Donna travel to Pizza House for lunch?_____

   _____

   _____

5. From Pizza House, how would Gail and Donna travel to the boat ride?_____

   _____

   _____

(continued)

On the Trip Activity (continued)

6. From the boat ride, how would they travel to the fishing pier?

   _____

   _____

   _____

7. From the fishing pier, how would Gail and Donna travel to
   their motel?_____

   _____

   _____

8. From the motel, how would they travel to the Fish House
   for dinner?_____

   _____

   _____

Visiting New Places

Gail and Donna went to the Marine Museum. Inside, they saw this sign:

INFORMATION	FIRST FLOOR LOBBY
AQUARIUM VIEW	FIRST FLOOR EAST WING
DEEP SEA CREATURES	FIRST FLOOR ROOM 101
OLD SHIPS	SECOND FLOOR WEST WING
SEA TREASURES	SECOND FLOOR ROOM 201
MAMMALS OF THE SEA	SECOND FLOOR ROOM 202
OCEANOGRAPHY	SECOND FLOOR ROOM 203
GIFT SHOP	FIRST FLOOR WEST WING
CLASSROOMS	BASEMENT EAST WING
AUDITORIUM	BASEMENT WEST WING

Read the questions. Write the answers in the blanks.

1. Where are the classes held?_____

_____

2. Where would Gail and Donna find gifts?

_____

_____

3. Where would Gail and Donna buy a book about the ocean?

_____

_____

(continued)

Visiting New Places (continued)

4. Donna read a story about treasures found in the ocean. Which room in the museum would have something about treasures?_____

   _____

5. Gail has an aquarium at home. She wants to see a real salt-water aquarium. Where would she go?

   _____

   _____

6. Which room displays oceanography, or the study of the sea?_____

   _____

7. Where could Donna learn more about ships of long ago?

   _____

   _____

8. Write down the rooms you would like to visit.

   _____

   _____

   _____

   _____

Visiting New Places Activity

This is a page from Donna and Gail's Tourist Guidebook. Read the page.

Points of Interest

☐ **The Art Center** — A collection of art work. Ocean Paintings. Open 10:00 A.M. to 4:00 P.M.

☐ **Beach Home Tour** — See the first homes built on this ocean. A walking tour starts every 10 minutes from 9:00 A.M. to 2:00 P.M.

☐ **Old Beach Lighthouse** — Walk all the way up! Open from 9:00 A.M. to 7:00 P.M.

☐ **Ocean Park Zoo** — See the animals of the area—and much more! 10:00 A.M. to 5:00 P.M.

Oceanside General Information	
State Police	480–1011
Fire	911
Minor Emergency Clinic	223–4116
Doctors' Building	622–4117
Time	633–4333
Weather	771–6050
Coast Guard	396–3000

782-3007

(continued)

Visiting New Places Activity (continued)

Answer the questions below.

1. Where could Donna and Gail go to see some of the oldest homes on the beach?_____

_____

2. If Gail cut her foot on the beach, what number could she call?_____

3. Donna wants to buy a painting of the beach. Where could she go and during what hours? _____

_____

4. Which number would Gail and Donna call to find out about any problems with boats at sea?_____

_____

5. Where could they go to tour a real lighthouse?

_____

6. Which could they see first: Beach Home Tour or the Ocean Park Zoo?_____

_____

7. What number would Gail or Donna dial if their motel was on fire? _____

8. The second morning of their trip, Donna's watch stopped. What number could she dial to set her watch?

_____

Decorating a Room

Tony just found out that he is moving. He went to see his new room in his new house. This is what Tony saw:

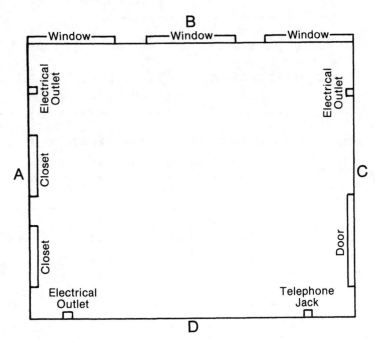

Read the questions. Write the answers in the blanks below.

1. Tony has a full-size bed. Do you think he would be able to

    put his bed against wall A? _____

2. Where do you think Tony should place his bed?

    _____

3. Tony has a large desk. He puts a lamp on the desk. Should

    he put the desk against wall B? _____

    Why? _____

    _____

    Where would you put the desk? _____

    _____

(continued)

Decorating a Room (continued)

4. Tony has a night table. He places a radio on the night table. Where should he put the night table?

_____

5. Tony has many pictures. Which wall or walls should Tony

hang the large pictures on?_____

_____

6. Tony has a stereo in a narrow cabinet. Where could Tony

place the stereo?_____

_____

7. Write any ideas you have to help Tony fix up his room.

_____

_____

_____

_____

8. Add any furniture you think Tony would like in his room. Be sure to think where the furniture would go in the room.

_____

_____

_____

_____

_____

_____

_____

Decorating a Room Activity

Cut out the furniture shapes from the sheet of paper your teacher will give you. Arrange the furniture in the room shown below. Then answer the questions.

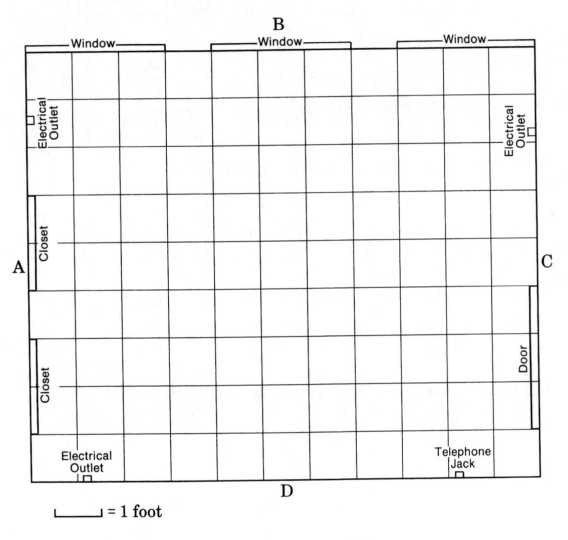

⌊____⌋ = 1 foot

1. How wide is Tony's room?_____

2. How long is Tony's room?_____

3. Which wall is the largest wall for hanging pictures?

_____

(continued)

Decorating a Room Activity (continued)

4. If you were buying carpet for this room, you would need to know the width and length. What size carpet would you need?

   _____

5. About how many feet wide is Tony's desk?

   _____

6. About how large is the rug?_____

   _____

7. Is the night table or the telephone table wider?

   _____

8. Are there many different ways to arrange the furniture?

   _____

   Arrange the room the way you like best.

9. About how wide are the windows?_____

   _____

10. If the windows are 72″ long or tall, which size shade would fit the best? Draw a line under the best answer:

    a. 24″ × 80″

    b. 36″ × 80″

    c. 44″ × 72″

(continued)

Decorating a Room Activity (continued)

Your teacher will give you a sheet of paper with shapes of furniture on it. Select the furniture you would like to have in your dream room. Cut out the pieces. Arrange the furniture below.

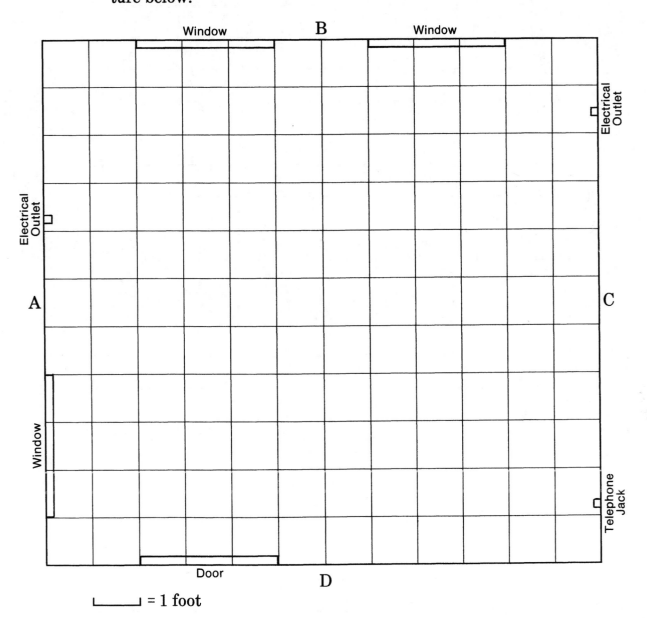

= 1 foot

(continued)

Decorating a Room Activity (continued)

Tell why you arranged the furniture the way you did:

_____

_____

_____

_____

_____

_____

_____

_____

_____

_____

_____

_____

_____

_____

_____

_____

_____

_____